ADVANTAGE Grammar

8

Table of Contents

Table of Contents

CREDITS

Concept Development: Kent Publishing Services, Inc.

Written by: Loretta Schorr

Editor: Thomas Hatch

Design/Production: Signature Design Group, Inc.

Art Director: Tom Cochrane

Project Director: Carolea Williams

Introduction

The **Advantage Grammar** series for grades 3-8 offers instruction and practice
in key writing skills, including

- grammar and usage
- capitalization and punctuation
- spelling
- writing good sentences
- writing good paragraphs
- editing your work

Take a look at all the advantages this grammar series offers . . .

Strong Skill Instruction

- The teaching component at the top of each lesson
  provides the support students need to work through the
  book independently.

- Plenty of skill practice pages will ensure students master
  essential skills they need to become competent writers.

- Examples, models, and practice activities use content from
  across the curriculum so students are learning about social
  studies, science, and literature as they master writing skills.

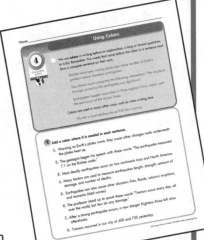

Editing Your Work pages provide for mixed practice of skills in a format
that supports today's process approach to the teaching of writing.

Take a Test Drive pages provide practice
using a test-taking format such as those included
in national standardized and
proficiency tests.

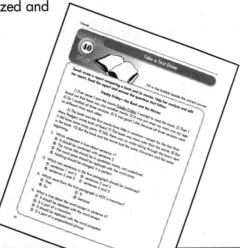

Name _____

LESSON

1

THE MEN BEHIND
THE LEGENDS:
JEFFERSON,
FRANKLIN, AND
ADAMS

Using Participles to Modify and Describe

 Participles are forms of verbs that can act as adjectives. They describe the words they modify by conveying a sense of action or a way of being.

The flag flutters in the breeze.   The **fluttering** flag is red, white, and blue.

The **confused** student read Benjamin Franklin's *Pennsylvania Gazette*.

Present participles end in **-ing** to convey current time.

When the student reads Franklin's *Pennsylvania Gazette*, he says, "It is **confusing**."

Past participles usually end in **-ed** to convey past time.

The **frustrated** student read Franklin's *Pennsylvania Gazette* again.

Perfect participles are formed by combining present and past participles to convey action taken over a length of time in the past.

Having published the *Pennsylvania Gazette* for many years, Benjamin Franklin retired.

Although they act as adjectives, participles are still verb forms and can be used with adverbs and objects, and they can form phrases.

Moving aggressively, Franklin wrote about current issues in his *Gazette*.
Seizing the moment, Franklin wrote about controversies.

Tips: When you use participles, you add expression and depth to your writing. You also help clarify your meaning, thereby enhancing your reader's ability to understand you.

A **Draw a line from the underlined participle to the noun or pronoun it describes or modifies.**

1. Experimenting with science, Franklin created the lightening rod.

2. Franklin, participating as a delegate at the Constitutional Convention, did not agree with many of the others' stated ideas.

3. Advocating for a presidential committee instead of a single executive, Franklin voiced his opinion.

B Complete the sentences with the present or past participle of the verb in italics.

1. The work *exhausted* Franklin and the delegates. It was _____ work.

2. The delegates were *exhausted*. The _____ delegates kept working.

3. The news of Washington's election *surprised* Franklin. It was

   _____ news.

C Complete the sentence with the present or past participle of the verb in parentheses.

1) My father was a delegate to the Constitutional Convention in the (thrive)

_____ city of Philadelphia. 2) I traveled with my (excite)

_____ mother and father to the great city, and my father was

able to get us into the hall.   3) I watched quietly, (thrill) _____

to see famous men like Franklin. 4) As the (preside) _____

officer, George Washington was popular. 5) In school, my teacher read to us from

Franklin's (interest) _____ work, *Poor Richard's Almanack*.

6) He is certainly a (fascinate) _____ and (respect)

_____ man!

D Rewrite the sentence so that the word that is modified comes right after the participle phrase.

1. Challenging to all of us, we were awed by Franklin's words.

   _____

   _____

Name _____

L E S S O N

THE MEN BEHIND
THE LEGENDS:
JEFFERSON,
FRANKLIN, AND
ADAMS

Compound Subject/Verb Agreement

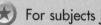 For subjects joined by **and**, use a plural verb.

Thomas Jefferson, Benjamin Franklin, and John Adams **are** founding fathers.

For subjects joined by **or** and **nor**, the verb agrees with the subject closest to it.

John Adams or Thomas Jefferson **is** worthy of further study.

A representative or delegates **are** eligible to speak at the Constitutional Convention.

For subjects joined by **either…or** and **neither…nor**

- if the compound subject is created with **singular words**, use a singular verb.

Neither Benjamin Franklin nor Thomas Jefferson **is** alive today.

- if a compound subject is created with **plural words**, use a plural verb.

Either visitors or students **are** able to access their speeches.

- if a compound subject is created with both singular and plural words, the verb must agree with the subject closest to it.

Neither the teacher nor the students **are** free to attend the workshop.

Either the students or the teacher **is** free to attend the workshop.

Insider's Tips

- When **each, every, many a,** or **many an** come before subjects joined by **and,** use a singular verb.
- **As well as, together with, in addition to, besides, including,** and **along with** are <u>not</u> conjunctions. They are modifiers—they do <u>not</u> connect, and they do <u>not</u> create compound subjects.
- Don't be confused by phrases or clauses inserted between your subject and verb!

A Circle the correct form of the verb for each sentence.

1. History, law, literature, architecture, science, and philosophy (was were) of interest to Thomas Jefferson.

Advantage Grammar Grade 8 © 2005 Creative Teaching Press

2. Neither his aristocratic background nor his European travels
(explain explains) Jefferson's development as a revolutionary.

3. His parents and his professors at the College of William and Mary
(play plays) a role in his growth and outlook, too.

4. The Enlightenment and the French Revolution (need needs) to be added to
the list of philosophies and events that had an impact on Jefferson.

5. Neither his writing nor his presidency (express expresses) the true measure
of the man.

6. His interest in the American West and his American-French relations
(prompt prompts) his purchase of vast lands from France.

7. With Jefferson's blessing, William Clark and Meriwether Lewis (set sets)
out to explore these lands west of the Mississippi.

8. Each explorer and leader (predict predicts) a successful journey, but neither
Clark nor Lewis (speak speaks) about the trials they will face.

9. Foreign policy and a long-term relationship with a slave (taint taints)
Jefferson's legacy.

10. Worship and belief (was were) sponsored by the state until Jefferson's
Statute of Virginia for Religious Freedom became law.

B **Select the proper form of the verb and complete the sentence.**

1. Neither Franklin nor Jefferson (promote promotes) _____

_____

2. Either the senator or the mayors (travel travels) _____

_____

3. Adams and Jefferson (believe believes) _____

_____

4. Jefferson as well as Franklin (draft drafts) _____

_____

5. Many a rumor and a myth (destroy destroys) _____

_____

Using Varied Sentence Types

LESSON

3

THE MEN BEHIND THE LEGENDS: JEFFERSON, FRANKLIN, AND ADAMS

⭐ Read these paragraphs and think about which is more interesting.

     1. Benjamin Franklin was a genius. He was one of America's founding fathers. Franklin was a printer and newspaper publisher. He was also the author of a popular book of advice called *Poor Richard's Almanack*. Benjamin Franklin was also a scientist and inventor.

     2. Often called a genius, Benjamin Franklin was one of America's founding fathers. What is he known for? Although Franklin made his living as a printer, newspaper publisher, and author of *Poor Richard's Almanack*, a popular book of advice, he is also celebrated as a scientist and inventory. He even experimented with electricity!

The sentences in paragraph 1 are all simple sentences. They are all declarative sentences of virtually the same length. In fact, the subject and the verb are the same in every sentence! This writing is static, and it can be boring to read.

The sentences in paragraph 2 are all different. The first one starts with an introductory clause. The second one is an interrogative sentence, and the third one is a compound-complex sentence. The final one is an exclamatory sentence. This writing is more dynamic, and the style helps to engage the reader's attention.

To make your writing more dynamic and to enhance your reader's interest, use varied sentence types.

 A Read the paragraph and follow the directions to revise it.

    1) Benjamin Franklin's image is on the $100 bill. 2) This founding father signed all three major documents. 3) These documents helped to free the colonies from British rule. 4) They are: the Declaration of Independence, the Treaty of Paris, and the United States Constitution. 5) This one man also helped to define how a good citizen should act. 6) He is also credited with founding or helping to form numerous organizations and institutions such as hospitals, libraries, and insurance companies; he was driven by a strong sense of civic duty.

1. Change sentence 1 into an interrogative sentence. _____

_____

Name _____

2. Combine sentences 2, 3, and 4 to make one sentence. _____

_____

_____

3. Rewrite sentence 5 to make it an exclamatory sentence. _____

_____

_____

4. Split sentence 6 into two sentences—one long and one short. _____

_____

_____

B **Complete the revisions to make the sentences more varied and the writing more interesting.**

Original

1. Thomas Jefferson wrote the first draft of the Declaration of Independence. Benjamin Franklin revised Jefferson's draft of the Declaration of Independence.

2. Fifty-five representatives signed the Declaration of Independence. Benjamin Franklin was one of the signers.

3. Franklin was an elderly man of 81 and in frail health at the Constitutional Convention. He was still intellectually alert. He advocated that executive power should not be placed in the hands of one person.

Revision

1. Although Thomas Jefferson wrote the first draft of the Declaration of Independence, Benjamin Franklin

_____.

2. Benjamin Franklin was one of the signers of the Declaration of Independence. How many _____ it? Fifty-five _____ !

3. At the Constitutional Convention, Franklin advocated that executive powers should not be placed in the hands on one person. He was _____

_____

_____

_____ !

Name _____

THE MEN BEHIND
THE LEGENDS:
JEFFERSON,
FRANKLIN, AND
ADAMS

⭐ A **hyphen** is a short line, either handwritten or typed like this -.

A **dash** is a long line, either handwritten or typed like this – or —.

When do you use a hyphen?

- To divide words between syllables at the end of a line.

    After graduating from Harvard College, John Adams emerg-
    ed as a political leader before the Revolutionary War.

    Tip: Do not break E-mail or URL addresses, numbers written as numerals,
    contractions, or proper nouns. Start them on the next line.

- To show a range of dates or pages.

    Read about the Adams' presidency (1797-1801) on pages 14-18.

- To write numbers as words.

    twenty-eight   one hundred thirty-two

- With prefixes **ex-, self-,** and **all-** as well as any prefix used with a
capitalized word.

    ex-wife   self-absorbed   all-knowing   anti-American

- With compound adjectives when they appear before the noun they modify

    Adams was a president in the eighteenth century.
    Adams was an eighteenth-century president.

When do you use a dash?

- To interrupt a sentence to introduce a related, but different, thought or to
emphasize a point.

    When your thought ends the sentence, use one dash.
    John Adams was a powerful speaker and an advocate—and the
    husband of Abigail Smith, a formidable woman.

    When your thought appears in the middle of a sentence, use two dashes.
    John Adams—the husband of Abigail Smith, a formidable
    woman—was a powerful speaker and an advocate.

A **Correct the following sentences by adding hyphens or dashes where needed.**

1. John Adams, along with his cousin Samuel Adams, helped to secure the appoint ment of George Washington as commander of the new army.

2. Was Adams sixty two when he became president?

3. Before becoming our second president, Adams served as our country's first vice president (1789 1797).

4. Abigail Adams' letters witty, vivid, and written just as she spoke tell the story of a woman who struggled with the hardship of war.

5. As a First Lady, Adams fulfilled her duties willingly even in the primitive conditions in the new capital of Washington, D.C., in 1800.

B **Two students took a grammar test. Here are their answers. Indicate whether each answer is correct (C) or wrong (W).**

	Student 1	Student 2
1. Write 28 as a numeral.	XXVIII	twenty-eight
2. Is "self-knowledge" punctuated correctly?	yes	no
3. How could you hyphenate the word "intimidate" at the end of a line?	intimi-date	in-timidate
4. Do you need a hyphen or dash in this sentence? If so, where? "Abgail Adams died in 1818 before her son John Quincy Adams became president (1825 1829)."	hyphen (1825-1829)	dash —her son—
5. Do you need a hyphen in this sentence? If so, where? "Adams, Jay, and Franklin negotiated the Treaty of Paris to end the eight year Revolutionary War."	no	yes eight-year
6. What's wrong with this sentence? "President Adams—stubborn and opinionated was a patriot and scholar, but he was an unpopular president."	nothing	you need a dash after the word *opinionated*

Name _____

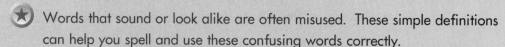

LESSON

5

THE MEN BEHIND
THE LEGENDS:
JEFFERSON,
FRANKLIN, AND
ADAMS

(★) Words that sound or look alike are often misused. These simple definitions can help you spell and use these confusing words correctly.

Advice/Advise—*Advice* is a noun that means "information"; *advise* is a verb that means "to recommend."

Capital/Capitol—As a noun, a *capital* is the city where the government is located, a sum of money, or the large-sized letter. As an adjective, *capital* means "foremost" or "chief." The building where government representatives meet is called a *capitol*. The building where the United States Congress meets is called the *Capitol*, and it is always written with a capital letter.

Complement/Compliment—*Complement* means "goes with" or "matches." *Compliment*, when used as a noun, means "a flattering remark"; as a verb, it means "to praise."

Device/Devise—Use *device* as a noun that means "a plan" or "a scheme" or "a specific effort." Use *devise* as a verb that means "to work out, create, or invent."

Discreet/Discrete—If you are *discreet*, you know how to keep a secret and be private. *Discrete* conveys a sense of separateness, not being attached to anything else, distinct.

Ensure/Insure/Assure—When you *ensure*, you make certain. When you *insure*, you protect against loss. When you *assure*, you give confidence to someone.

Envelop/Envelope—*Envelop* is a verb that means "to cover or wrap." Envelope is what you put a letter in to mail it.

Guest/Guessed—Your *guest* is a visitor. *Guessed* is the past tense for the verb *guess*.

Incite/Insight—*Incite* is a verb that means "to arouse"; *insight* is a noun that means "understanding."

Legislator/Legislature—A *legislator* is the person that makes laws. A *legislature* is the entire body of lawmakers.

A **Circle the word that completes the sentence correctly.**

1. Thomas Jefferson (deviced devised) the Declaration of Independence to firmly state why the colonies were breaking away from England.

2. The Declaration of Independence (ensured assured insured) that the new Americans would have rights and freedoms.

3. The Declaration served to (incite insight) Great Britain to punish the rebellious colonists.

4. Historians know a lot about President John Adams and his wife Abigail because of the many letters they mailed to one another in (envelops envelopes).

5. Abigail Adams was an independent woman and did not hesitate to (advice advise) her husband about issues of the day.

6. Benjamin Franklin wasn't (discrete discreet); he lobbied France to enter the Revolutionary War on the side of the Americans.

7. New York, New York, was the first (capital capitol) of the United States; then, the (legislators/legislatures) moved to Philadelphia where they stayed until in 1800.

8. Did you (guest guess) that Thomas Jefferson was a wealthy landowner?

9. If you called Benjamin Franklin a "revolutionary," would he take it as a (complement compliment)?

B **If the underlined word in each sentence is correct, mark the sentence with a C. If it is not correct, mark it with an X.**

_____ **1.** You would require political <u>incite</u> to know why Thomas Jefferson did not consider slaves when he wrote, "all men were created equal."

_____ **2.** The Declaration of Independence was not <u>discrete</u> when it concluded, "these united colonists are, and of right ought to be, free and independent states."

_____ **3.** A <u>guest</u> of King George III of England would have witnessed the monarch's fury when he read those words.

_____ **4.** Jefferson employed four literary <u>devices</u> when he wrote the Declaration of Independence.

_____ **5.** Jefferson wanted to <u>insure</u> that King George received a definitive message.

_____ **6.** What <u>advise</u> would Benjamin Franklin have given to colonists who wanted to remain loyal to King George III?

_____ **7.** The men (including 81-year-old Franklin) who attended the Constitutional Convention in 1787 were called delegates, not <u>legislatures</u>.

_____ **8.** To say that Franklin was one of the most influential men during the birth of our nation would be the truth, not just a <u>compliment</u>.

_____ **9.** Where would the new American leaders get the <u>capital</u> to finance the new government?

6

THE MEN BEHIND
THE LEGENDS:
JEFFERSON,
FRANKLIN, AND
ADAMS

Rewriting to Correct

⭐ The process of writing requires several steps: generating the idea, conducting any research necessary, organizing the material, developing an outline, writing, checking for errors, rewriting, checking for expression and meaning, and rewriting. Here are some tips to help you with one of those steps: checking for errors.

- Use the computer as a spelling checker, then manually check your work. The computer will not pick up word usage problems. Verify the spelling of any proper nouns.
- Look up an unknown word's definition.
- Review your subject-verb agreement for accuracy.
- Make sure each sentence is a complete sentence and not run-on or a fragment.
- Examine your sentences to identify any misplaced modifiers.
- Verify that you have used the correct form of punctuation as well as formatting such as italics and underlining.
- Double-check the accuracy of any numbers, dates, names, titles, and other factual information.
- Determine if you have left out any essential information from your notes, research, or outline.

Ⓐ **Read the following paragraphs and answer the questions.**

1) Although Benjamin Franklin never served as president of the United States, he greatly influenced the course of hour history. 2) One of his most significant contributions were in the diplomatic arena.

3) In 1776, Franklin was in Paris acting as the colonies' Minister to France. 4) In that role, France negotiated an alliance with the colonies. 5) He understood that this alliance would be important to the colonies' ability to win the revolution against Britain? 6) His knowledge of the French and his personal connections enabled him to secure loans from this ally. 7) This support helped to finance the revolution.

8) As America's Revolutionary War neared an end, France wanted to arrange for a three-way treaty because they, too had been at war with Great Britain. 9) Franklin was eager to comply, seeing an opportunity to further cement relations with the French and influence their negotiations with Great Britain involving portions of the North American continent. 10) Several Americans, however, wanted to negotiate directly with Britain. 11) In fact, the new Americans.

12) Franklin had to use all his diplomatic prowess and connections to address France's ill feelings.

   13) In the end, at the Treaty of Paris in 1676, the pact was signed and sent to the U.S. Congress for ratification.   14) Thanks to Franklin's skills, along with Adam's and Jay's work, the United States was recognized as a nation by the world's great superpowers, France and Great Britain.

1. Which sentences have punctuation errors? _____

2. Which sentence has an incorrect date? _____

3. Rewrite sentence 4 to correct the misplaced modifier.

   _____

   _____

4. Which sentence is a fragment? _____

5. Rewrite sentence 2 to correct the subject-verb agreement.

   _____

   _____

6. What is the definition of *prowess* in sentence 12? Is it used correctly in this sentence? If not, why not?

   _____

   _____

   _____

   _____

7. Identify the error in sentence 1.

   _____

8. Based on the facts in the fourth paragraph, what information is missing from the third paragraph?

   _____

   _____

LESSON

Editing Your Work

7

THE MEN BEHIND
THE LEGENDS:
JEFFERSON,
FRANKLIN, AND
ADAMS

Editing your work is an important step in the writing process. Many tests ask you to show what you know about editing.

A **Read the paragraph and answer the questions that follow to edit it.**

1) Benjamin Franklin (1706:1790) was a businessman and a scientist. 2) He was also a diplomat, inventor, and a founding father of our nation. 3) If you asked Benjamin Franklin what he was, however, he would answer, "a journalist!" 4) His publications as well as his experience is diversified. 5) He took great pride in his contributions as a printer and publisher.

6) Many a respecting expert and professor credit him with founding modern journalism. 7) Prior to Franklin, newspapers were published to express only one viewpoint. 8) In fact, he grew up during a time when no one could openly criticize the King of England or his representatives. 9) Some newspapers are still a <u>devise/device</u> for organizations to advance their agendas. 10) Most, however, do try to report the news in an unbiased manner with coverage of [oppose] _____ viewpoints.

11) Much of Franklin's success, scholars say, can be traced to his willingness to examine all sides of an issue. 12) Believe in a free and open press, Franklin set the foundation for excellence and tolerance in the profession. 13) He was often criticized for doing so. 14) He responded to some of that criticism in his now-famous article, "Apology for Printers," which stated, "…when truth and error have fair play, the former is always an overmatch for the latter." 15) What <u>advise/advice</u> would Franklin have for journalists today?

1. Correct the punctuation error in sentence 1. _____

_____

_____

2. Rewrite sentences 1, 2, and 3 to vary the sentence types.

_____

_____

_____

_____

_____

_____

3. Correct the subject-verb agreement in sentence 4.

_____

_____

_____

4. In sentence 5, how would you hyphenate *publisher* if it fell at the end of
   a line? _____

5. In sentence 6, is the participle correct? If not, what should it be?

_____

_____

6. What else is wrong with sentence 6?

_____

_____

_____

7. Select the correct word to complete sentence 9.

_____

8. Based on the verb in brackets, fill in the blank in sentence 10 with a participle
   to describe *viewpoint*.

_____

9. Identify the error in sentence 12.

_____

_____

_____

10. Select the correct word to complete sentence 15.

_____

Take a Test Drive

Fill in the bubble beside the correct answer.

Lois wrote a report about the difficulties that John Adams faced during his presidency. Read her work and answer the questions that follow.

1) Gaining more votes than Thomas Jefferson or Thomas Pinckney, Washington was succeeded by John Adams. 2) During his administration (1797:1801), Adams faced several challenges. 3) He did not trust the imposing Alexander Hamilton. 4) Hamilton took action without advicing Adams. 5) Adams also faced a setback in the country's cherished relationship with France. 6) Responding to escalating political opposition, several controversies were created by Adams.

1. Which statement is true about sentence 1?
Ⓐ It contains a dangling participle phrase.
Ⓑ *Succeed* is used incorrectly.
Ⓒ It is correct.
Ⓓ The comma is not needed.

2. How should sentence 2 be changed?
Ⓕ Change the colon into a comma.
Ⓖ Change the colon into a hyphen.
Ⓗ Change the colon into a dash.
Ⓙ No change is needed.

3. Which statement is true about sentence 3?
Ⓐ *Imposing* is not used correctly.
Ⓑ *Imposing* is a participle.
Ⓒ *Imposing* is an adverb.
Ⓓ *Imposing* should be changed to *imposed*.

4. How should sentence 4 be rewritten?
Ⓕ Hamilton took actions without advicing Adams.
Ⓖ Adams took action without advicing Hamilton
Ⓗ Hamilton took action without advising Adams.
Ⓙ It is correct as is.

5. What is true about sentence 5?

   Ⓐ It is grammatically correct, but the content is inaccurate.

   Ⓑ It is grammatically correct, but it is too short.

   Ⓒ It is correct.

   Ⓓ It is incorrect.

6. Why does sentence 6 need to be corrected?

   Ⓕ The subject-verb agreement is wrong.

   Ⓖ It contains a dangling participle phrase.

   Ⓗ It needs another comma.

   Ⓙ It needs a dash.

During her research, Lois listed interesting facts about President Adams. Help her revise and edit her facts before she adds them to her report.

Relations with the French 1) The French tried to extort money from U.S. representatives in, what has been called—the XYZ Affair. 2) Americans became indignant. 3) Would the countries—once friends—go to war?

Relations with Hamilton 4) Responding to the threat of war, Adams wanted to increase the navy; Hamilton (1755—1804) advised many legislators to increase the army. 5) Using his influence as the former Secretary of the Treasury, Congress was persuaded by Hamilton to make him inspector general of the army. 6) He wanted to ensure he had capitol to fund it.

7. Which sentence uses the dash correctly?

   Ⓐ sentence 1   Ⓒ sentence 4

   Ⓑ sentence 3   Ⓓ none of them

8. How should sentence 5 be changed?

   Ⓕ Add a comma before *as*.

   Ⓖ Change *using* to *having*.

   Ⓗ Correct the dangling participle phrase.

   Ⓙ It should not be changed at all.

9. Which word is used incorrectly in these research notes? What should the correct one be?

   Ⓐ ensure - assure   Ⓒ advised - adviced

   Ⓑ capitol - capital   Ⓓ legislators - legislatures

Pronouns and Antecedents

⭐ A pronoun is a word that takes the place of a noun—a person, place, or thing. **She**, **it**, and **they** are pronouns, and words such as **many**, **these**, and **everyone** can also be pronouns. Before choosing a pronoun when writing, ask, "What does this pronoun refer to?" In other words, what is the pronoun's **antecedent**—the word it represents? A pronoun can come before or after its antecedent in a sentence or paragraph.

> President Lincoln was assassinated on the eve of the complete Union victory.
>
> **He** is known for providing superior leadership skills for the war effort.

Lincoln is the antecedent for the pronoun **he**. A pronoun must agree in word and number with its antecedent. If the antecedent is single, the pronoun must be singular. If the antecedent is plural, the pronoun must be plural, too. When an antecedent is clear, the message is clear.

A Circle the correct antecedent for the underlined pronoun.

1. The Missouri Compromise was signed in 1820, and <u>it</u> is often credited for being a prelude to the Civil War.

2. Although <u>it</u> occurred more than 40 years after the Missouri Compromise, the secession crisis resulted in armed combat.

3. Lee, Grant, Jackson, and Sherman were among the dozen prominent figures of the Civil War. <u>They</u> were strategic and tactical military leaders.

4. Robert E. Lee led the battle at Richmond. <u>He</u> was a newly appointed general.

B Circle the pronoun in the parentheses that completes the sentence.

1. Nearly four million African-Americans were freed from (their his) slavery.

2. A state did not have the right to withdraw (themselves itself) from the union.

3. The Civil War claimed more than 600,000 lives, but many issues were left unaddressed at the end of (them it).

4. Slaves were now free, but how would (they it) fit into the new society?

  Advantage Grammar Grade 8 © 2005 Creative Teaching Press

★ Compound antecedents can cause problems when choosing pronouns. When two or more antecedents are joined by **or, nor, either...or,** and **neither...nor,** the pronoun should agree with the closest antecedent. If the closest antecedent is single, the pronoun will be single; if it is plural, the pronoun will be plural.

Neither Thaddeus Stevens nor other generals have been given their due respect as leaders.

To clarify your meaning, you may have to avoid the use of pronouns.

Robert E. Lee invited Jefferson Davis to the meeting because he enjoyed planning.

Is Robert E. Lee or Jefferson Davis the antecedent for he? It isn't clear. To clarify, reword the sentence and eliminate the pronoun.

Robert E. Lee invited Jefferson Davis to the meeting because Lee enjoyed planning.

C **Complete each sentence with a pronoun that agrees with the underlined antecedent.**

1. <u>Dorothea Dix and Rose Greenhow</u> played active roles in the Civil War, but

   _____ contributions were very different.

2. <u>Greenhow</u> was a spy for the Confederacy, a role for which _____ was jailed.

3. Either Dorothea Dix or <u>Clara Barton</u> could be honored for _____ nursing work on the battlefields of the Civil War.

D **Rewrite each sentence to clarify its meaning.**

1. The victorious general was elated, but he kept <u>it</u> contained.

   _____

2. The new orders arrived late. <u>They</u> wanted the soldiers to surrender, not attack.

   _____

L E S S O N

10

THE CIVIL WAR

Comparatives and Superlatives

⭐ Adjectives are words that describe people, places, and things. How are adjectives used to express comparison? There are two forms: **comparative** and **superlative**. When writing, choose the correct form of the adjective to express your exact meaning.

Use the comparative form when comparing **two** people, places, or things.
- Add **-er** to the end of the adjective if it is a small word.
- Use **more** with the adjective if it is a long word.

> The number of soldiers killed in the Civil War was great**er** than the number who lost their lives in the Vietnam War.
> Is there **more interest** in studying the Civil War than the Vietnam War?

Use the superlative form when comparing **more than two** people, places, or things.
- Add **-est** to the end of the adjective if it is a small word.
- Use **most** with the adjective if it is a long word.

> The students couldn't agree which battle was the **most influential** in the Civil War, but all knew which battle was the long**est**.

A **Complete each sentence with the correct comparative or superlative form of the adjective in parenthesis.**

1. (short) Lincoln's Gettysburg Address in 1863 to honor those slain was his

   _____ speech.

2. (inspiring) Many historians feel that the speech is the _____ one in American history.

3. (close) Although Lincoln was _____ to the radical wing of his party than the conservative branch, he named men from both groups to his cabinet.

4. (smart) Although he had little formal education, Lincoln is thought to be one

   of the _____ presidents we have ever had.

Name _____

When adding the suffix **-er** or **-est** to many words ending in **y**, first drop the **y** and add **i**. For example, **ugly** would be expressed as **uglier** or **ugliest**. When adding the suffix **-er** or **-est** to some words ending in **d**, double that final letter. For example, **mad** would be written as **madder**.

Some words have special forms to express comparison:

adjective	to compare two	to compare more than two
good	better	best
bad	worse	worst

B **Cross out the mistake in each sentence. Write the correct word or words.**

1. Lincoln wrote five versions of the Gettysburg Address. Was the final the better one?

   _____

2. Who was tallest, President Clinton or President Lincoln?

   _____

3. What is the more valuable lesson to be learned from the Civil War?

   _____

4. Who was the best debater, Abraham Lincoln or Stephen Douglas?

   _____

C **Enter the correct form of the six missing adjective in the boxes.**

original word	comparative form	superlative form
difficult	more difficult	1.
slow	slower	2.
3.	more valuable	most valuable
silly	4.	silliest
happy	5.	happiest
bad	worse	6.

Parallel Construction

THE CIVIL WAR

⭐ To organize your thoughts and express yourself clearly, use parallel construction. It's good grammar, and it adds impact to your writing. Here's how to create **parallel construction** in your writing:

Repeat a word within a sentence. Repeat nouns, adjectives, verbs, and phrases to build a parallel structure.

> The Civil War was **very** long, **very** costly, and **very** deadly.
> The war was about fundamental issues—government of the **people**, by the **people**, and for the **people**.

Build a series of sentences with similar structure and style. Each sentence contains the same words, and all words stick to the simple pattern: subject-verb-phrase.

> **He fought in the** woods. **He fought in the** mountains. **He fought in the** valleys.

Sentence type and word repetition result in parallel construction. Each question starts, continues, and ends the same way.

> **When would** the armies retreat? **When would** the war end? **When would** the soldiers return?

Parallel construction is also a matter of good grammar. This sentence is not grammatically correct because *difficult* is an adjective, but *expense* is a noun.

> Lincoln's strategy for war was **difficult** and an **expense**.

To correct it, make sure adjectives are paralleled by adjectives, nouns by nouns, and so on.

> Lincoln's strategy for war was **difficult** and **expensive**.

Be careful when writing a series of verbs, too.

> wrong   The soldiers loved **getting** letters from home, **hearing** the generals speak, and **to receive** their pay.

> right   The soldiers loved **getting** letters from home, **hearing** the generals speak, and **receiving** their pay.
> or
> The soldiers loved **to get** letters from home, **to hear** the generals speak, and **to receive** their pay.

A Circle the answer that corrects or creates parallel construction in each sentence.

1. During a period of 86 years, the United States recovered from the Revolutionary War, endured the Civil War, and had fights with American Indians.

   a. change **war** to **War**

   b. change **Revolutionary War** to **revolutionary war**

   c. delete **a period of**

   d. change **had fights with** to **battled**

2. Slaves were born in bondage, worked in bondage, and died enslaved.

   a. change **born** to **bought**

   b. delete **enslaved**

   c. change **enslaved** to **in bondage**

   d. add a comma after **born**

3. A Civil War soldier received little medical care, only a small amount of food, and little hope.

   a. delete **medical**

   b. replace **only a small amount of** with **little**

   c. capitalize **soldier**

   d. change **little hope** to **some hope**

B Fill in the blanks in the letter to create parallel construction.

Dear Wife,

Soon, we will go into battle, my first this week. We are so close to the Union boys, we can hear them laughing, see them _____ , and watch them praying. I miss my farm. I miss my _____ . I miss my home. Do you think of me? Do you watch for me? _____ pray for me? Please continue to write. I get your letters weeks late, but I get them. I _____ them. I cherish them.   Please sell what you can to keep the cotton in the field, the children _____ , and the hope in our hearts.

Parentheses and Brackets

⭐ Parentheses ( ) and brackets [ ] are always used as a pair (one to open and open to close).

Use parentheses to set off information from the main idea. When readers see parentheses, they know they are getting **extra** information.

> The cities of Charleston and Savannah (popular with tourists today) played influential roles in the Civil War.

To clarify a number, put it in parentheses.

> Nearly one thousand (1,000) Southern women became nurses in the Confederate army.

To organize a series, add numbers in parentheses to the sentence.

> For the Confederacy, three reasons for going to war were: (1) to assert states' rights, (2) to maintain the institution of slavery, and (3) to protect an agricultural way of life.

When parentheses appear at the end of the sentence, place the punctuation mark to end the sentence **outside** the closing parenthesis.

> Did Lincoln go back to Springfield to practice law at the end of his Congressional term (1847-1849)?

Tip on Writing with Parentheses: If the information surrounded by the parentheses was left out of the sentence, the sentence would still make sense.

Use brackets when the information in parentheses has extra details. Place the closing bracket inside the closing parenthesis mark.

> The general who was responsible for the victory (Irvin McDowell [1818-1885]) was never given proper credit.

Use brackets with quoted material to tell the reader when you have deliberately changed or added something in another person's writing or speech.

> The historian wrote, "The date of the battle is *equally* as important as the time of the battle." [italics added]

A If the placement of parentheses is correct in the sentence, write C on the line. If the placement of parentheses is not correct, write X.

_____ 1. In debates, Lincoln argued that the federal government (not individual states) had the right to prohibit slavery in the western territories.

_____ 2. By the time Lincoln was inaugurated in 1861, six states (Mississippi, Florida, Alabama, Georgia, Louisiana, and Texas) had seceded from the Union.

_____ 3. The Confederacy (the Confederate States of America) became the name for these six rebellious states.

_____ 4. Not (everyone many farmers) couldn't afford slaves in these states that supported secession.

_____ 5. Although the North had several advantages more industry, railroads and people, (the South had more experienced generals).

_____ 6. Intense fighting started near Bull Run (July 21, 1861) in Virginia.

_____ 7. At Bull Run 30 miles from Washington, D.C., (35,000 Union troops) faced 25,000 Confederate soldiers.

_____ 8. A naval blockade of Southern ports (the Confederate economy was dependent upon sale of cotton and tobacco to Europe) was essential to Lincoln's war strategy.

_____ 9. At least five new technologies contributed to the brutality of the war: (1 firearms, 2 explosives, 3 railroads, 4 submarines, and 5 ironclad ships).

B If the placement of brackets is correct in the sentence, write C on the line. If the placement of brackets is not correct, write X.

_____ 1. Although the Compromise of 1850 (California entered the Union [as a free state) avoided a crises, no one was satisfied.

_____ 2. The signing of the Kansas-Nebraska Act [introducing the doctrine of popular sovereignty [1854]) led to violence.

_____ 3. *Uncle Tom's Cabin* [Harriet Beecher Stowe (1811-1896)] was a best-selling but controversial novel.

_____ 4. Many wanted the territories acquired from Mexico (Mexican-American War [1846-1848)) to ban slavery.

LESSON

13

THE CIVIL WAR

Frequently Misspelled Words, M-Z

⭐ Words that sound or look alike are often misused. These simple definitions can help you spell and use these confusing words correctly.

Principal/Principle—*Principal* means "the first idea or thing in rank" or the "top person," while *principle* means "a rule," "essential quality," or "fundamental law or doctrine."

Proceed/Precede—*Proceed* means "to carry on" or "continue," but *precede* means "to go before."

Proffer/Prefer—*Proffer* means "to offer or propose," and *prefer* indicates that one thing is more to your liking than another.

Succeed/Secede/Supersede—*Succeed* means "to triumph," while *secede* means to "tear apart from" and *supersede* indicates "being replaced."

Tenet/Tenant—*Tenet* is a "belief or doctrine," but a *tenant* is a person who pays rent.

Thorough/Through—*Thorough* indicates you have done all you can, while *through* indicates "passage."

Troop/Troupe—*Troop* is a "group," but *troupe* refers to a specific group, namely, a group of actors, singers, or other entertainers.

Unconscious/Unconscientious—*Unconscious* indicates mindlessness or a lack of intention, while *unconscientious* indicates a lack of care or precision.

Woman's/Women's—*Woman's* indicates possession for one woman; *women's* indicates possession for more than one woman.

A **Underline the word that completes the sentence correctly.**

1. The (troops troupes) welcomed any relief from the combat of war.

2. The (principal principle) of states' rights was one of the motivating factors for war.

3. Bragg's defeat at Chattanooga, a major communications and transportation center for the Confederacy, (proceeded preceded) his removal from command.

4. Many historians claim that the (principal principle) reason for going to war was not the eradication of slavery.

5. Was the so-called Trent Affair, the Union's removal of two Confederate diplomats from the British merchant vessel Trent, a deliberate or an (unconscious unconscientious) effort to embroil Britain in the Civil War?

6. Merchants selling provisions often accompanied Union (troops troupes).

7. In the Confederacy, (woman's women's) primary roles during the Civil War were to maintain and defend the homestead.

8. What was the first state to (succeed secede) from the Union?

9. One of the benefits (proffered preferred) to freed slaves was the right to legalize marriages.

10. To be believed, a (woman's women's) efforts to disguise herself as a male soldier would have to be (thorough through).

11. The (tenet tenant) that women had a special moral gift to preserve society and keep the home pure was prevalent in both the North and South before the war.

12. A total of 237 U.S. Naval officers resigned to serve the Confederacy. If you were born in the South, would you (prefer proffer) to serve the Union or Confederacy?

B **The following is a fictitious diary entry made by a woman living in the Confederacy during the waning days of the Civil War. Complete this story by filling in the blanks with the correct word from the list on page 28.**

Last week, a _____ settled in a pasture just outside of town. I sold some of them carrots and onions from the garden yesterday. Bad news! Several of my slaves escaped that night. I know they went to join the performers. It's no surprise that they could _____ the pleasure of the road to the rigors of plantation life. I never thought a _____ role would be so hard. Since my husbands and sons and brothers are off at war, however, I must _____ without them. I must be _____ in my approach to keeping our farm and homestead productive. Doing so gets more trying each day, but when they do return, I want them to be proud of the job I've done. It would be so much easier to be _____ , but I must be attentive to detail and _____ despite all odds. I just want my men home with me. The ladies in town are sewing quilts for our returning heroes—and I'm sure they will be triumphant. I chose the following _____ to feature on my quilt, "Home is where the heart is." It's a _____ I cling to in these dark days of despair.

Rewriting for Expression

★ To be effective, your writing should clearly express your ideas. Develop the habit of editing your work for grammar, spelling, usage, and orderly flow. These tips will also help you to improve your writing and to express yourself clearly.

Choose active, not passive verbs.

passive	The debate will be won by Lincoln
active	Lincoln will win the debate.

Add dialogue or quotations.

Lincoln's words, "a house divided against itself cannot stand," still have meaning today.

Be descriptive.

The green grass of the battlefield was trampled by boots caked in dark brown mud.

Vary sentence length and type.

The generals planned the strategy for months, but they failed to take into account the weather which can be brutally cold at that time of year. The strategy failed.

Avoid clichés.

cliché	The general's orders will arrive any old day now.
better	The general's orders will arrive within the next few days.

 A **Read the following paragraph, then make the changes and corrections indicated on the next page.**

The Harsh Lives of Slaves

1) After all that's said and done, some former slaves were still alive in 1930. 2) Information we have today about slavery comes from the slaves' oral histories compiled by the Federal Writers' Project. 3) Slaves could not own property or vote, and it could not sign a contract. 4) One former slave explained how 50 to 100 lashes with a whip was a regular punishment. 5) To stabilize the workforce, some slaves were encouraged by their slave owners to marry and have families, but most slaves lived in dread of being sold and separated from their spouses and children. 6) Many families were disrupted. 7) It is estimated that

 Advantage Grammar Grade 8 © 2005 Creative Teaching Press

perhaps as many as one-third of slave marriages were ended by slave owners. 8) Personal freedoms were restricted, work conditions were dangerous, and living conditions were primitive. 9) Most worked in the fields, but slaves also acted as house servants, nannies, blacksmiths, carpenters, and weavers, even factory and dock workers. 10) What was best: working on the farm or in the factory? 11) Nearly seventy 70 percent of the white population in the South in 1850 did not own slaves. 12) Those that did, however, lived a privileged life; they believed they were fulfilling their duty to educating themselves, keep slaves, and pursue leisure time and culture.

1. Underline the cliché in sentence 1.

2. Add a descriptive word to modify the noun underlined in sentence 2.

3. Correct the error in sentence 3.

4. Rewrite sentence 4 to change it into a quotation.

_____

_____

5. Change the passive voice to the active voice in sentence 5.

_____

_____

6. Transform sentence 6 into a question.

_____

_____

7. Change the passive voice to the active voice in sentence 7.

_____

_____

8. Rewrite sentences 8 and 9 to create three sentences of varying lengths.

_____

_____

_____

9. Correct the error in sentence 10.

10. Add parentheses where they belong in sentence 11.

11. Underline the error in parallel construction in sentence 12.

Name _____

 Editing your work is an important step in the writing process. Many tests ask that you show what you know about editing.

A **A teacher asked her students to write a summary of their Civil War studies to present to their parents. Here's what one student wrote. Read the paragraph and answer the questions below.**

1) No sooner had we finished studying the Revolutionary War, then we started to read about the Civil War. 2) First, we studied the roots of the war, including the principle reason for states succeeding. 3) President Lincoln (1809-1865] steered the Union during this trying time. 4) We studied his biography, reading his speeches, and review his policies. 5) One essay question we had to answer was, "Who was the better president, Lincoln or Johnson and why?" 6) I wrote that each man contributed their talents to help the country.

1. Underline the cliché in sentence 1, and rewrite the sentence to eliminate the cliché.

   _____

   _____

2. Underline the two errors in sentence 2, and rewrite the sentence to correct the errors. _____

   _____

3. What is wrong in sentence 3? _____

4. Rewrite sentence 4 to create parallel construction. _____

   _____

5. Is sentence 5 correct? If not, why not? _____

   _____

   _____

6. Circle the error in sentence 6, and explain why it is wrong. _____

   _____

Name _____

B Your teacher returned this essay to you. Rewrite the essay to correct all of the errors she indicated.

not parallel

Most slaves were severely punished for disobeying their owners or <u>try to escape</u>.

break the second sentence into two to vary your sentence lengths
Nat Turner was one slave who tried to revolt against slavery, but his efforts failed.

He was enslaved in Virginia, and he was also a preacher to his people. At first,

when did this start? add a date
seven slaves joined the revolt; but over the next two days, they were soon joined by

watch your pronoun!
75 other slaves. Turner's owner, Joseph Travis, and its family were killed, and a

total of 50 white people were murdered. Six weeks later, Turner was captured and

wrong word
hanged, and the revolt was put down by a troupe of 3,000 citizens.

_____

_____

_____

_____

_____

_____

_____

_____

_____

Name

Take a Test Drive

LESSON

16

THE CIVIL WAR

Fill in the bubble beside the correct answer.

Jennifer wrote a report on the Civil War. Help her revise her work. Read the paragraphs and follow the directions.

Reconstruction

1) In its Gettysburg Address, President Lincoln said, "Now we are engaged in a great civil war, testing whether that nation, or any nation so conceived, and so dedicated, can long endure." 2) Part of our nation's test came after the war during Reconstruction 1865-1877). 3) Lincoln didn't live to see how the states became united again around our principals.

1. Which statement is true about sentence 1?
   Ⓐ Lincoln died before he gave the Gettysburg Address.
   Ⓑ The word *conceived* is not used properly.
   Ⓒ There are too many commas.
   Ⓓ The use of the pronoun *its* is incorrect.

2. What is missing from sentence 2?
   Ⓕ the word *Civil*
   Ⓖ a parenthesis before the first date
   Ⓗ a comma after *war*
   Ⓙ a subject

3. How should sentence 3 be changed?
   Ⓐ Change *principals* to *principles*.
   Ⓑ Capitalize *states*.
   Ⓒ Eliminate the word *how*.
   Ⓓ Change nothing—it is correct.

Advantage Grammar Grade 8 © 2005 Creative Teaching Press

Continue helping Jennifer improve her writing. Read her next paragraph and answers the questions below.

4) It was up to President Andrew Johnson to unite the country after the Civil War. 5) His plan called for each state to form its new government, create its constitution, and freeing its slaves. 6) Some states passed black codes (restricting the former slaves' ability to travel, change jobs, and vote), but all states in the South had rejoined the Union by 1870. 7) After the war, Southern agriculture was in shambles, cities were in chaos, and railroads ruined.

4. Which statement is true?
    (F) Sentence 6 is a simple sentence.
    (G) Sentence 4 is correct.
    (H) Sentence 5 needs another comma.
    (J) Sentence 7 is correct.

5. How should sentence 5 be corrected?
    (A) Capitalize the word *state*.
    (B) Eliminate the comma after *government*.
    (C) Change *his plan* to *he*.
    (D) Change *freeing* to *free*.

6. Which statement is true about sentence 6?
    (F) It is a simple sentence.
    (G) Not all the states had joined by 1870.
    (H) The use of parentheses is correct.
    (J) It shouldn't be included in this report.

7. Which statement is true?
    (A) Sentence 7 is incorrect.
    (B) Sentence 7 is correct.
    (C) Sentence 7 is too long.
    (D) Sentence 7 needs parentheses.

17

THE INTERNET

Identifying Parts of Speech

⭐ The eight parts of speech are: verb, noun, pronoun, adjective, adverb, conjunction, preposition, and interjection.

He said to me, "Wow! Plagiarism is always illegal."

Pronoun-verb-preposition-pronoun, "Interjection! Noun-verb-adverb-adjective."

Adverbs can be troublesome. Adverbs answer **when, where, why, in what manner,** or **to what extent.** Adverbs can be single words, phrases, or clauses.

Tip 1: Adverbs modify verbs, adjectives, or other adverbs.

Tip 2:. Most adverbs that describe action verbs end in **-ly**.

Tip 3: If the verb already expresses the meaning, do not add an adverb.

incorrect:	You can continue on with what you were doing.
correct:	You can continue with what you were doing.

 A **Identify the part of speech of the underlined words in the following sentences.**

1. Some <u>experts</u> <u>describe</u> plagiarism as "intellectual theft" <u>and</u> "cheating."

2. The Internet <u>makes</u> it easy to "cut and paste" material with the click <u>of</u> a mouse.

3. "<u>Yes</u>!" the student thought, "I know it is that easy!"

4. Teachers <u>have</u> many <u>good</u> sources to help them <u>easily</u> spot plagiarism.

5. One way to avoid plagiarism is to cite <u>your</u> source.

6. <u>You</u> can also paraphrase and <u>attribute</u> the <u>material</u> to the author.

Advantage Grammar Grade 8 © 2005 Creative Teaching Press

B **Answer the questions based on this passage.**

1) Teachers spend hours fighting deception. 2) Some read everything with a cynical eye. 3) By copying from experts, students' writing can sound far more sophisticated, and the plagiarism can be spotted easy. 4) Others use search engines to find suspect phrases. 5) Teachers are turning eagerly to computerized tools. 6) Some school districts are first beginning to subscribe to detective companies. 7) Services like these provide teachers with detailed reports about sections of text copied verbatim from the Internet. 8) They quick provide the link to the sources.

1. Combine sentences 1 and 2 by adding a conjunction.

    _____

    _____

2. Correct the error in sentence 3.

    _____

    _____

3. What part of speech is *suspect* in sentence 4?

    _____

4. Identify the adjective and adverb in sentence 5. _____

5. Correct the error in sentence 6.

    _____

    _____

6. Correct the error in sentence 8, then combine sentences 7 and 8 by adding the conjunction *not only…but also*.

    _____

    _____

    _____

7. What part of speech is *search* in sentence 4? _____

8. What is the preposition in sentence 8? _____

9. Does sentence 4 contain a preposition? _____

10. What are the nouns in sentence 6? _____

Name _____

Independent and Dependent Clauses

18

THE INTERNET

⭐ Unlike phrases, all clauses have a subject and a verb. Independent (main) clauses can stand alone because they express a complete thought. A dependent (subordinate) clause cannot stand alone. Here are some examples:

- one independent clause   **The Internet has changed our lives.**
- two independent clauses   **The Internet has changed our lives,** but not every change has been a good one.
  Notice that both clauses can stand alone and still make sense.
- one independent clause + one dependent clause   **The Internet can change our lives, if we know how to make the most of it.**
  Notice that the first clause can stand alone, but the second cannot.

There are three types of dependent clauses. Most begin with a conjunction or relative pronoun.

- An **adjectival clause** modifies a noun or pronoun and usually begins with *who, whose, whom, which,* or *that.*   The Internet, **which you can access through a browser,** has revolutionized communications.
- A **noun clause** answers the questions *who, whom,* or *what,* and can play many roles in the sentence. It often begins with words such as *if, how, where, when, why,* etc.
  A browser is **how you access the Internet.**
- An **adverbial clause** modifies a verb, adjective, or noun and answers *when, where, how, why, under what condition,* and *to what extent?* Words such as *after, although, because, until,* and *while* introduce these clauses.
  You can access the World Wide Web **when you sign up for an ISP.**

A **Underline all the dependent clauses in the following sentences.**

1. AOL, which you can subscribe to, is one of the largest Internet Services Providers.

2. If you want a community experience, you can join AOL or any other large ISP.

3. A screen name, which your ISP enables you to select, identifies you online.

4. You can use a number of screen names when you search the Web.

5. Some screen names are obvious, but some do not make sense until you examine them.

B If the sentence contains a dependent clause, mark it as *D*; if it does not, mark it with *X*.

_____ 1. When I first started using the Internet, I used a funny screen name.

_____ 2. Unfortunately, I had to switch to a new ISP and couldn't continue with that name.

_____ 3. That name was so amusing to my friends; they made jokes about it whenever I saw them.

_____ 4. My dad didn't think it was funny, and he was glad that we had to switch to a new ISP.

C Write a complete sentence for each of the following dependent clauses. You can place the dependent clause in any position in the sentence—beginning, middle, or end.

1. when you first log on _____

_____

2. although you will need your privacy _____

_____

3. if you select your own name _____

_____

4. which you can choose when you subscribe _____

_____

D Identify the dependent clauses in the following sentence by marking *N* for noun, *ADJ* for adjectival, or *ADV* for adverbial.

_____ 1. Internet Explorer, which is available through Microsoft, is one of the popular Net browsers.

_____ 2. When you choose a browser, you might also want to consider Netscape Navigator.

_____ 3. Whether the browser fits your needs remains to be seen.

_____ 4. Do you think that any browser is adequate?

LESSON

19

THE INTERNET

Relating Ideas

⭐ Clauses and phrases help you express yourself clearly. Let's look at clauses and phrases that help you express a clear relationship between ideas. *Reminder: A clause has a subject and a verb; a phrase does not.*

- **Essential** (restrictive) clauses and phrases change the meaning of the sentence. Do not set them off with punctuation.

    The claim **that "blogs are chit chat"** does not adequately define blogging today.

- **Nonessential** (nonrestrictive) clauses and phrases add to, but do not change, the meaning of the sentence. Set them off with punctuation—commas, dashes, or parentheses.

    A blog, **which is short for "Web log,"** is well written, but informal.

- **Appositive phrases** are noun phrases used to modify a noun.

    George Allen, **a senator from Virginia,** is among a group of lawmakers trying to permanently ban taxes on Internet access.

A Underline the appositive phrases in the following sentences.

1. One blogger, a lawyer, uses his blog to comment on legal cases and issues of law.

2. The pioneering blogger, a Harvard fellow and founder of successful technology companies, presented at a conference on blogging.

3. Dan Gillmore, a *San Jose Mercury News* columnist, has a blog.

4. A grassroots movement, blogging is not yet being embraced by business.

5. One chief technology officer, a prolific Web surfer, has traded e-mailing for blogging.

B **Identify the phrase or clause in each sentence as *E* for essential or *N* for nonessential.**

_____ **1.** The blog, which is linked to his Web site, now appears on search engine results.

_____ **2.** Search engines favor sites that are updated frequently.

_____ **3.** Reporters that search the Web find his site easily thanks to his blog.

_____ **4.** I found a blog that I liked.

_____ **5.** His personal blog, which included essays and trivia, was more popular than his business log.

_____ **6.** You can also access portal-like blogs, which aggregate content and offer links to individual blogs.

_____ **7.** Blogging may be a way to provide knowledge-management services, which help customers enhance their effectiveness.

_____ **8.** A recommended-reading list, a standard feature for most blogs, is one of her favorite sources for new sites and blogs.

C **Add punctuation, where needed, to correct this passage. Before you add punctuation, determine if a clause or phrase is essential or nonessential to the meaning of its sentence.**

After 9-11-01, some New Yorkers who lived and worked around the World Trade Center kept online journals to relate their experiences. These blogs drew millions of readers because they were eyewitness accounts. You, too, can keep a blog if you are interested. When you build your blog, however, you should not expect millions of readers! In fact, readers will not return to your blog unless you keep it current.

There are many technical tools that you can access to build and maintain your blog if you find the time to devote to blogging. Unless your research indicates otherwise you can keep your blog fairly simple. There are three types of blogs—microjournal, notebook, and filter; and you can start one with the help of a blogging service provider where you can create an account in minutes. If you have the confidence and the ability you can also create a blog with software which gives you options to use movable type, link to other sites, search, and index.

Commas and Semicolons

20

THE INTERNET

⭐ Want to express yourself clearly? Use commas and semicolons correctly!

Use a comma to:

- separate items in a series

  A hoax is a practical joke, an exaggeration, a rumor, or a malicious lie. Many hoaxes have resulted in financial loss for companies, their customers, and their stockholders.

- set off a phrase or clause

  On the Internet, hoaxes are known as "net lore." As far as the Internet is concerned, don't believe everything you read! Go to www.urbanlegends.com, one of the most popular sites on the Web, to determine what's a hoax.

- separate independent clauses when using *but* or *and*

  Some hoaxes are harmless fun, but others are spread with deliberate intent to destroy people or companies.

- introduce a direct quotation

  Some hoaxes prey on people's worst fears and others twist the truth to leave people scratching their heads and asking, "Can that be true?"

Use a semicolon to:

- separate independent clauses without *but* or *and*

  E-mail messages can forward information easily to hundreds of receipts; they are ideal for spreading cyber-hoaxes.

- separate items in a series when a comma or commas are used in that series

  To spot an E-mail hoax, look for statements such as "forward this to every one you know," "this is not a hoax," and "this is true"; determine whether the sender wrote the message; read the message carefully; and cross-check the claim with legitimate news or reference sources.

Caution: Comma Splice!

Avoid adding a comma where none is needed.

Experts say companies should respond quickly to Internet rumors, and enlist the help of an objective party to explain why the rumor is false.

Notice that the sentence does not contain two independent clauses—just a compound verb (*respond* and *enlist*)—and does not need a comma. Delete the comma or add a subject, making two independent clauses.

Experts say companies should respond quickly to Internet rumors, and they should enlist the help of an objective party to explain why the rumor is false.

Add a comma or commas to the following sentences where needed.

1. What causes someone to generate a hoax on the Net: boredom stupidity or evil intent?

2. The Securities and Exchange Commission which is worried about stock manipulation online has investigated and charged many who have posted bogus press releases about corporate earnings.

3. A Net rumor about dihydrogen monoxide commonly known as water caused a city in California to panic and pass a law banning materials made with the substance!

B **Add a semicolon to the following sentences where needed.**

1. One persistent hoax alerted people to a proposed E-mail tax another claimed that Honda was giving away free cars.

2. Some hoaxes mask viruses consume space within your mailbox, causing you the inconvenience and time to shift through E-mail and spread fear.

3. You may have received a hoax convincing you to delete a necessary operating file, claiming it was a virus to send money or to submit personal information, claiming you have won a prize.

4. Sites such as truthorfiction.com, snopes.com, and hoaxbusters.ciac.org can help you be a hoax-buster you can even refer to symantec.com/avcenter/hoax to verify virus hoaxes.

C **Circle the comma splices in the following sentences.**

Internet hoaxes fall into different categories. One preys on emotions. An emotional appeal on behalf of a child dying of cancer asked people to donate money, and wanted them to forward the E-mail to friends. Another appeals to greed. One company's stock soared when an Internet rumor was spread about a corporate takeover, and fell when it denied the rumor. Some of these greed-based appeals cheat people out of money, take their personal information, and trick them into surrendering passwords. Some hoaxes capitalize on people's desires for good deals. Take, for example, the hoax that Disney World, Microsoft, and The Gap would reward people for forwarding E-mail to their friends. These companies do not track our E-mail, but focus on their real business.

Building Words from Foreign Roots

LESSON

21

THE INTERNET

⭐ Did you know you can speak and read Greek and Latin? Yes, you can! Many of our words are taken from other languages and still have Greek and Latin roots.

In the following paragraph, *reacted, enacting,* and *action* have roots in Latin; **-act** means "do."

> The music industry has **reacted** to increased piracy by urging Congress to take **action**. On the state and federal levels, our representatives are **enacting** laws to curb Internet piracy.

Greek or Latin root words can be used as prefixes and suffixes. For example, the Latin roots **-merge** or **-mers** both mean "dip." Add them to the prefix **sub**, meaning "under," and you form **submerge** and **submerse**, meaning "dip" or "go under."

When you know the meaning of the word's root, you can build your vocabulary and enhance your reading comprehension.

 Using the word in Column A as a clue, identify the correct meaning of the root. Draw a line from the root in Column B to its meaning in Column C.

A	B	C
Sample Word	**Root**	**Meaning**
agriculture	*agri*	circle
amble	*ambul*	opinion
aquarium	*aqua*	hold
bibliography	*biblio*	heat
bicycle	*cycl*	water
dogmatic	*dogma*	shape
uniform	*form*	ask
question	*ques*	field
contain	*tain*	walk
thermal	*therm*	book

 Advantage Grammar Grade 8 © 2005 Creative Teaching Press

Name _____

B Based on the clue words in Column A, write the meaning for the root word.

A	B	C
Sample Word	**Root**	**Meaning**
astronaut, asterisk	*ast*	
audience, audition	*aud*	
credit, incredible	*cred*	
predict, verdict	*dic*	
diameter, barometer	*meter*	
dismiss, missile	*miss*	
pedestrian, pedestal	*ped*	
portable, import	*port*	
erupt, bankrupt	*rupt*	
inspect, respect	*spec*	

C Write a word in Column C that contains the root in Column B. Use the meaning clues in Column A to help you.

A	B	C
Meaning	**Root**	**Sample Word**
roll	*volv*	
empty	*vac*	
city	*urb*	
see	*scop*	
end	*term*	
land	*terr*	
twist	*tort*	
build	*struct*	
sound	*phon*	
health	*san*	

D Write the root for the sample words. Use the meanings provided in Column A to help you.

A	B	C
Meaning	**Sample Words**	**Root**
field	campus, camp	
head	decapitate, captain	
go	exceed, proceed	
sure	certify, ascertain	

22

THE INTERNET

Transitions in Writing

⭐ When we speak, we use gestures and facial expressions to help the listener follow our train of thought. For example, through body language, we can let them know when we are finished with one subject and on with the next! When we write, **however**, we do not have these physical clues to help us communicate. **Instead**, we use transitional words and phrases within sentences and to begin or end paragraphs and sentences. Without transitions, your writing will be stiff and boring. **Therefore**, use transitional words and phrases to help you express yourself logically and clearly. Here are some examples:

• to call attention	in fact, certainly, namely, indeed
• to change the topic	another, in addition, in contrast, however
• to compare or contrast	on the contrary, on the other hand, otherwise, even so, conversely
• to convey sequence and time	then, next, still, following, after, before, at first, later, simultaneously
• to draw conclusion	therefore, as a result, as you can see, without a doubt, thus, in summary, accordingly
• to give examples	for example, to clarify, for one thing
• to relate cause and effect	consequently, with this in mind, as a result

 A **Underline all the transitional words or phrases in the following paragraph.**

"Without a doubt, I need a guide to cyberspace," said Drew's father in frustration when he subscribed to an Internet Service Provider. Before long, Drew found just the thing his father needed—a book called *The Young Surfer's Guide to Cyberspace*. Before Drew could even show him the chapters in the book, his father protested, "But that's for kids!" As a result, Drew explained just how much the book had helped him when he received it for a birthday present. He pointed out how it helped him save hours of time. For example, he learned about news groups and found great information for reports. Otherwise, he would have spent hours going to the library looking for the same data. "Okay, I'll take a look," his dad said finally. "Looks like I need help."

B For each of the following sentences, create a second, new sentence using the underlined transition word. You can use the transition word at the beginning, middle, or end of your sentence.

1. <u>clearly</u> He visited nationalgeographic.com/education/homework to see

   the "photo of the day." _____

   _____

2. <u>eventually</u> He had trouble with searching online. _____

   _____

3. <u>in spite of</u> At *Ask Jeeves* for kids, ajkids.com, you can find study tools

   as well as the latest reviews of video games. _____

   _____

4. <u>for instance</u> She used spellcheck.net for homework. _____

   _____

5. <u>first</u> How should the student conduct research online? _____

   _____

C Complete the following sentences by adding a transitional word or phrase where indicated.

_____ homework, I visit the "Photo and Arts" section at

nationalgeographic.com/education/homework. The site challenges me to

guess what a photo is. Clues in a scrolling box help me identify the photographs.

_____ , I can check my answers. For homework help,

_____ , I search the other sections, _____ ,

"History" and "Science."

23

THE INTERNET

Editing Your Work

Editing your work is an important step in the writing process. Many tests ask you to show what you know about editing.

Sanjay wrote this essay about how people use the Internet. Read the essay and answer the questions that follow to help him edit it.

Use and Misuse

1) Decades ago, students enjoyed pranks such as putting "kick me" signs on their friends' backs. 2) Today, practical jokes are played on the Internet; often, they are not funny at all. 3) Many people receive bogus messages regarding a new virus. 4) Others get promotions in their mailbox that sound too good to be true. 5) Maybe you saw the photo of a man holding a cat as large as a big dog. 6) Did you believe that nuclear radiation caused the cat to grow so large?

7) How else do students use the Internet? 8) Some use the Internet to plagiarize the work of others. 9) Plagiarism is illegal. 10) How can a student include the ideas and opinions of others without plagiarizing? 11) Instead of copying another's work word-for-word, students can learn to paraphrase the material, attribute the material with quotations that acknowledge the original author, or comment on the original work.

12) Internet abuse is music piracy. 13) In early 2004, the FBI first began to seize more than 200 computers and 30 servers. 14) Attorney General John Ashcroft reported that one server contained over 65,000 pirated music titles; this cannot be dismissed as an exception.

15) The Motion Picture Association is also alarmed over the rising theft of film, and software manufacturers are unhappy about theft of their programs.

16) Increasingly, people are using their work computers which often have high-speed, broadband connections to download digital files.

17) The Recording Industry of America, a music industry group, has sued hundreds of people for copyright infringement. 18) Reuters News Agency reports that the International Federation of the Phonographic Industry, which represents major music companies, is contacting companies to enlist their help in stopping this abuse. 19) Companies are helpful they do not want their employees wasting company time to perform downloads.

1. Rewrite sentences 3 and 12 to add a transitional phrase.

_____

_____

_____

_____

2. Identify the transitional words in sentences 2 and 16.

_____

3. What part of speech are the words *reports, sued,* and *contacting*?

_____

_____

4. What word should be deleted in sentence 13?

_____

5. What part of speech is *rising* in sentence 15, and what word does it modify?

_____

6. Underline the dependent clause in sentence 18. Is it an essential or nonessential clause?

_____

_____

7. Underline the independent clause in sentence 11.

8. Correct the punctuation in sentence 16? Why is it incorrect?

_____

9. Correct the punctuation error in sentence 11. Why is it incorrect?

_____

10. Correct the punctuation error in sentence 19.

11. What two words in sentence 14 have foreign roots?

_____

L E S S O N

24

THE INTERNET

Take a Test Drive

Fill in the bubble beside the correct answer.

Glen was researching information about the Internet. He jotted down on note cards three passages that he found. Read his notes and answer the questions that follow.

1) You are being duped and you should ignore the message as a hoax. 2) Real viruses are spread on the Internet and it is a good practice never to download and open an attachment from a stranger. 3) Be skeptical and visit several sites when you need to verify a hoax. 4) The museumofhoaxes.com contains stories of rumors and tall tales from as far back as the 1700s, and features a "Gullibility Test."

1. What statement is true about sentence 1?
  Ⓐ It needs a comma.   Ⓒ It needs a colon.
  Ⓑ It needs a semicolon.   Ⓓ It is correct.

2. What statement is false about sentence 2?
  Ⓕ It needs a comma.   Ⓗ It is incorrect.
  Ⓖ It has two independent clauses.   Ⓙ It is correct.

3. How can you correct sentence 4?
  Ⓐ Change the comma to a semicolon.   Ⓒ Add a comma after *rumors*.
  Ⓑ Delete the comma.   Ⓓ Add a semicolon after *rumors*.

4. Which statement is false about sentence 5?
  Ⓕ *Submit* has a foreign root.
  Ⓖ *Submit* does not have a foreign root.
  Ⓗ The meaning of the root for *submit* is *send*.
  Ⓙ The root for *submit* is *mit*.

               Advantage Grammar Grade 8 © 2005 Creative Teaching Press

5) <u>Today</u>, the Internet makes it easier than ever for students to plagiarize and submit the work of others as their own. 6) How can teachers be certain a work or parts of a work are plagiarized? 7) How can teachers ascertain whether or not students' submissions are really their own?

5. Which statement is true about sentences 6 and 7?
  Ⓐ **Certain** and **ascertain** have the same root.
  Ⓑ **Certain** and **ascertain** do not have the same root.
  Ⓒ **Ascertain** is not used correctly.
  Ⓓ **Certain** is not used correctly.

6. In sentence 5, the underlined word is:
  Ⓕ a noun.
  Ⓖ incorrect.
  Ⓗ a transitional word.
  Ⓙ out of place.

8) After I successfully started a personal blog, I decided to learn more HTML to add formatting, which helps the reader clearly understand my ideas, to my blog. 9) With this in mind, I searched the Web for HTML lessons and visited my library to see if it had books on the subject. 10) In fact, I finally found the perfect book; before I could read it, however, my friend called to tell me about blogging software. 11) It does the formatting for me! 12) Mastering the software was a snap; now, my only challenge is updating my blog to keep the content current.

7. Identify some of the transitional words in this passage.
  Ⓐ after, which, however
  Ⓑ after, however, in fact
  Ⓒ decided, searched, called
  Ⓓ lessons, ideas, subject

8. Identify some of the adverbs in this passage.
  Ⓕ mastering, blogging, formatting
  Ⓖ snap, current, personal
  Ⓗ successfully, finally, clearly
  Ⓙ add, helps, does

9. In sentence 9, what part of the speech is *Web*?
  Ⓐ adverb
  Ⓑ adjective
  Ⓒ noun
  Ⓓ verb

10. In sentence 8, the words *which helps the reader clearly understand my ideas* is
  Ⓕ an independent phrase
  Ⓖ an independent clause
  Ⓗ a dependent phrase
  Ⓙ a dependent clause

Name _____

Identify Parts of Sentences

⭐ To be complete, a sentence must have a subject and a verb. To enhance the meaning of a sentence, however, we usually need an object.

1. The **direct object**, usually a noun, answers the questions *who*, or *what*. To find the direct object, say the subject and verb, then ask *who* or *what*.

<u>Edgar Allan Poe</u> <u>wrote</u> *<u>The Tell-Tale Heart</u>*.
　　subject　　　　verb　　　direct object

2. An **object complement** gives more information about the direct object, and it is usually a noun, pronoun, or adjective. To have an object complement, you must have a direct object.

<u>Dashiell Hammett</u> <u>created</u> the <u>detective</u> <u>Sam Spade</u>.
　　subject　　　　　verb　　　　object　 direct object
　　　　　　　　　　　　　　　　complement

3. The **indirect object** comes before a direct object and answers *to whom* or *for whom*. To find the indirect object, say the subject and verb, then ask *to whom* or *for whom*.

Hammett's *<u>The Glass Key</u>* <u>told</u> <u>us</u> an intriguing <u>story</u>.
　　　　　subject　　　　verb　indirect　　　 direct object
　　　　　　　　　　　　　　　　object

Two other parts of sentences that you should be familiar with are predicate adjectives and nominatives.

4. **Predicate adjectives** describe the **subject** and are located after **linking** or **sensing** verbs.

<u>Sam Spade</u> <u>seems</u> <u>tough</u>.
　subject　　sensing　predicate
　　　　　　　verb　　adjective

5. **Predicate nominatives** are **nouns** that give more information about the **subject**; they are located after **linking** or **sensing** verbs.

<u>Sam Spade</u> <u>is</u> my favorite <u>detective</u>.
　subject　　linking　　　　 predicate
　　　　　　　verb　　　　　 nominative

Name _____

A Identify the underlined part of the sentence as a direct object *(DO)*, an indirect objective *(IO)*, an object complement *(OC)*, a predicate adjective *(PA)*, or a predicate nominative *(PN)* by writing the abbreviation above the underlined word.

1) At first, Dashiell Hammett was a struggling <u>writer</u>. 2) Early in his career, Hammett was a <u>detective</u>, but he retired due to poor health and started writing scripts for radio. 3) He lived a tumultuous <u>life</u>. 4) He found <u>fame</u> when he wrote *The Thin Man* in 1934. 5) In *The Thin Man*, the main character investigates a <u>disappearance</u>. 6) Many of Hammett's books became <u>movies</u>. 7) The *Maltese Falcon* tells <u>readers</u> the intrigue caused by deceit and theft. 8) The character of Sam Spade was "<u>hard boiled</u>." 9) Although he only wrote five novels, Dashiell Hammett was an influential <u>writer</u>. 10) He defined the <u>spare</u> style of the modern detective novel.

B Underline the direct objects, predicate adjectives, and predicate nominatives in the following sentences.

1. Hammett's writing was spare, and his style influenced diverse writers.

2. Before Hammett, most mysteries were romantic.

3. The urban settings for his novels seemed realistic and gritty.

4. His detectives are isolated men.

5. He presented a violent view of American society.

Name _____

Commonly Misused Verbs

LITERATURE

⭐ **1. bring - take:** When you want to indicate motion towards the speaker, use **bring**. When you want to indicate motion away from the speaker, use **take**.

to speaker   When you return, **bring** me one of Rex Stout's mysteries.

away from speaker   When you go to class today, **take** the Rex Stout novel.

2. come - go: Use **come** when you want to show motion toward the speaker, and use **go** when you want to show motion away from the speaker.

to speaker   Mom said, "Don't **come** home from school without books."

away from speaker   Mom said, "Don't **go** to your room yet."

3. leave - let: All the forms of **leave** (leave, left, leaving) mean "to move away, abandon, or depart." All the forms of **let** (let, letting) mean "to permit or allow."

depart   The murderer **left** the scene by taxi.

permit   **Let** me read the ending first.

4. lie - lie - lay: When we use **lie** (lie, lied, lying) to express something that's not true, we usually do not run into any problems. The confusion occurs when **lie** (lie, lay, lain, lying) means "rest, recline, or stay." Do not confuse **lie** with **lay** (lay, laid, laying), which means "to place or put." **Lay** always takes a direct object; **lie** never takes a direct object.

direct object of verb

place/put   She was **laying** the <u>copy</u> of The Haunted Bridge on the desk.

rest/stay   She didn't see the thief **lying** under the bed. [no object]

Tip: Replace lay *with* place *to make sure you are using the correct verb.*

5. rise - raise: Use **raise** (raise, raised, raising) to mean "lift" or "mention." It always takes a direct object. Use **rise** (rise, rose, risen, rising) to mean "get up" or "move up by yourself." It never takes a direct object.

direct object of verb

lift   The detective **raises** <u>orchids</u>.

get up   Wolfe rarely **rises** from his chair in the office. [no object]

6. sit - set: When you use **set** (set, setting) to mean "place something somewhere," it always needs a direct object! Use **sit** (sit, sat, sitting) to mean "to be seated." It never takes a direct object.

direct object of verb

placing   She **set** the murder <u>weapon</u> on the floor.

"to be seated"   She **sat** in the most comfortable chair. [no object]

A Finish the sentences by circling the proper word.

1. "Before you (come   go)," the lawyer said, "(leave let) this DNA sample with me."

2. "No, I must (bring take) it, because I cannot (leave let) it out of my sight," the detective replied. "I cannot (set sit) it down for a moment."

3. Then, he (raised rose) from his chair and (left let) the room.

4. The lawyer turned to his client and said, "Well, that (rises raises) the question of whether or not we should have an expert to dismiss the importance of the evidence."

5. "I'm not lying, you know," the client replied, "I was (lying laying) on the floor of the closet when he fired—I didn't commit the murder!"

B Underline 10 errors in this paragraph and provide the correct word.

"How can I convince the jury of that!" Did he believe his client? He wasn't sure, but he could not let this meeting end without being certain of his innocence. After the meeting, he had to come to courtroom to defend the man, but he still needed evidence he could bring to the jury. He raised from his chair and went to the window.

"What's the problem?" the client asked.

"Go with me," the lawyer said suddenly. He turned away from the window and picked up his briefcase that was laying on the desk.

The client rose up, but then set right down again. "Hey, I have to rise a point," he said.

"There's no time," the lawyer said, lying his hand on the doorknob.

"Well, you cannot come back to that courtroom without me, can you?"

"You rise a good point," the lawyer said, sitting down again.

Using the Active Voice

⭐ Effective writers develop an **active voice**. In the active voice, the subjects of sentences take action; they are not acted upon. When you write with an active voice, you are helping your readers. They will want to read your writing. Make sure the subjects of your sentences are doers, not receivers, of action. Try to cultivate an active voice in your writing.

passive	The Nancy Drew series was written by Carolyn Keene.
active	Carolyn Keene wrote the Nancy Drew series.
passive	It was intended for Nancy Drew to investigate a mystery in each book.
active	Nancy Drew investigated a mystery in each book.

Stop, Look, Rewrite

If you find too many of the following phrases, words, or habits in your writing, stop and rewrite using a more active voice.

- **it is intended, it was decided**
- excessive use of the helping verb **to be**
- **were** + verb
- excessive use of **there**, **this**, or **that** as the subject

A Rewrite the paragraph using the active voice. Pay special attention to the underlined sentences.

1) <u>There is a heroine of a popular detective series called Nancy Drew.</u> 2) <u>The books were written by anonymous authors and were published under the pseudonym Carolyn Keene.</u> 3) <u>Many of the books early in the series were written by Mildred Wirt Benson.</u> 4) <u>More than 200 million copies of the Nancy Drew series have been sold worldwide by the Stratemeyer Syndicate.</u>

5) Who was Nancy Drew? 6) In the series, she lived with her father and housekeeper in a town called River Heights, and she solved mysteries in her neighborhood. 7) Nancy Drew had a cadre of friends at her side during her adventures. 8) <u>There were also her close friends who were the characters George Fayne and Bess Marvin</u>, and her boyfriend Ned Nickerson also lent his support.

  Advantage Grammar Grade 8 © 2005 Creative Teaching Press

Name _____

_____

_____

_____

_____

_____

_____

_____

_____

_____

_____

_____

_____

_____

_____

_____

B **Answer the following questions using sentences with active voice.**

1. Why were some of the books in the Nancy Drew series made into movies?

_____

_____

2. Why would the publisher include the character Nancy Drew in another series?

_____

_____

3. Why is it important for a publisher to update a series of books?

_____

_____

4. If you have read a Nancy Drew mystery, write a sentence telling why you liked—or didn't like—the book.

_____

_____

Editing for Punctuation and Capitalization

⭐ Punctuation and capitalization are the road signs of writing. **Periods and question marks** are "dead end" signs; they tell us we've come to the end. **Commas and semicolons** are the "yellow" lights of sentences; they tell us to slow down. **Hyphens and dashes** are "yield" signs; they tell us to pay attention to what's coming. **Parentheses and brackets** are like advertising signs on the side of the road. They tell us information that's good to know, but that's not necessary to the drive.

Other punctuation marks such as **colons and quotation marks** are "caution" signs; they call our attention to information. The proper use of capitalization is also critical to a reader's understanding. **Capital letters** help us identify the type of information we are receiving.

To enhance your writing, edit your work for proper use of punctuation and capitalization.

A **Read the following sentences and identify whether or not each sentence is punctuated correctly. Mark *C* if it is correct; mark *X* if it is wrong.**

_____ **1.** Today's detectives are often private investigators

_____ **2.** These investigators can be unmarried and many have other sources of income.

_____ **3.** In contemporary detective fiction, readers enjoy the character of the assistant who functions as a surrogate audience for the investigator.

_____ **4.** Charles Dickens' novel, *Bleak House* (1853, involves a sub-plot about a crime investigation.

_____ **5.** In *Bleak House*, suspects appear in disguise on the night of the murder, this confuses the detective.

_____ **6.** Poe used Paris as a setting for many of his "whodunit" stories; he enjoyed juxtaposing the wild nature of crime against the city's refinement and sophistication.

_____ **7.** In "The Narrative of Arthur Gordon Pym", the reader had to decipher strange writing.

_____ **8.** Philip Marlowe Mike Hammer, and Laura Principal were all amateur detectives and characters in popular novels.

_____ **9.** Didn't Agatha Christie write cookbooks, too.

_____ **10.** The names of authors who write about historical crimes are: Lindsey Davis, Umberto Eco, Robert van Gulik, Ellis Peters, and Steven Saylor.

B Add punctuation and capitalization where needed in each sentence.

1. edgar allan poe is the father of modern "whodunit" novels in the detective genre

2. his story "the tell-tale heart" presents a genuine mystery

3. to this day critics debate the solution of the mystery what did the murderer hear

4. the murderer was also the first-person narrator of the story

5. was it midnight or 3 am when he visited the old mans room

6. for days after he killed the old man the murderer was tortured by a hideous sound

7. he believed he heard the dead mans heart beating

C Write a book review about a detective novel or mystery you read and use the following marks of punctuation: period, comma, semicolon, question mark, hyphen, dash, and quotation mark. If you have not read a detective novel or mystery, create a mystery story incorporating those marks of punctuation.

_____

_____

_____

_____

_____

_____

_____

_____

_____

_____

LESSON

Alphabetizing Names and Titles

29

LITERATURE

⭐ To alphabetize words, compare letters in the same position in each word. If the first letter or word is identical, move on to the second, and so on. Here are some additional rules to alphabetize names and titles.

Proper names are alphabetized by last name, then first. Titles are the last unit of comparison.

Name	Unit 1	Unit 2	Unit 3
Nancy Drew	Drew	Nancy	
Nicholas Drew	Drew	Nicholas	
Ms. Nora Drew	Drew	Nora	Ms.
Senator Nora Drew	Drew	Nora	Senator

The first units are all the same, so look at the second units. **Na** in **Nancy** comes before **Ni** in **Nicholas**, which comes before **No** in **Nora**. So the order is **Na, Ni, No**. The two entries for **Nora Drew** are then broken down to Unit 3, the comparison of titles. In this example, the **M** of **Ms.** comes before the **S** of **Senator**.

How do you alphabetize titles that have prepositions and articles in the name? If a name starts with the articles *the, a,* or *an,* use the article as the last unit for comparison. If a names starts with prepositions such as of or in, treat the preposition as the first unit of comparison.

Here are some tips about alphabetizing titles that contain numbers:

- Titles that start with numbers come before titles that start with roman numerals.
- Titles that start with numbers and roman numerals come before titles that start with words.
- If a number in a title is spelled out as a word, alphabetize it as a word.

Name	Unit 1	Unit 2	Unit 3	Unit 4	Unit 5	Unit 6
16 Captive Witnesses	16	Captive	Witnesses			
The Mystery at Lilac Inn	Mystery	at	Lilac	Inn	The	
Mystery of Crocodile Island	Mystery	of	Crocodile	Island		
Of Mystery's Love	Of	Mystery's	Love			
Six Clues in the Jewel Box	Six	Clues	in	the	Jewel	Box

Advantage Grammar Grade 8 © 2005 Creative Teaching Press

A Alphabetize the following list of authors who write detective novels or stories, and show your work in the table:

G. K. Chesteron
Agatha Christie
Ms. Amanda Cross
Ms. Leslie Charteris
Raymond Chandler
Patricia Cornwell

Name	Unit 1	Unit 2	Unit 3

B Alphabetize the following titles which are based on Nancy Drew books and show your work in the table:

The Secret of the Old Clock
The Sign of the Twisted Candles
Strange Message in the Parchment
99 Steps
A Secret at Shadow Ranch
The Scarlet Slipper Mystery

Name	Unit 1	Unit 2	Unit 3

LESSON

30

LITERATURE

Excluding Extraneous Information

⭐ The topic sentence of a paragraph states the main idea. Supporting sentences explore more details or give examples. To enhance your writing, edit your work to eliminate information that is extraneous, in other words, information that is not needed or not "on topic."

The "whodunit" is the most popular form of the detective genre. In these books, the detective displays ingenuity to find clues, interview suspects, and reveal the method of the murder. He or she must undertake these tasks without revealing the murderer's identity to the reader until the end of the book. The first "whodunit" is often identified by many experts as "The Murders in the Rue Morgue," a short story created in 1841 by the poet and writer Edgar Allan Poe. <u>He wrote the famous poem, "The Raven."</u> His other "whodunits" were very popular during his time; they include: "The Purloined Letter" and "The Narrative of Arthur Gordon Pym."

In this example, the underlined sentence contains extraneous information. Poe *did* write "The Raven," but that information is not needed in a paragraph about the detective genre, "whodunit."

A **Read the following passage and underline the extraneous sentence in each paragraph.**

1. Many mystery and detective stories were published before Poe's time, and he drew popular motifs from them. For example, Poe incorporated conflict between official and private investigators. He was also not the first writer to use the idea of a crime happening in a sealed room or one based on an historical crime. Many fictional accounts have been written about the real-life criminal Jack the Ripper.

2. Despite the fact that his achievement is grounded in several decades of detective fiction, Poe's contributions to the genre are considerable. Not much is known about his personal life, however. Critics maintain that Poe introduced seven new elements: the bumbling or eccentric detective, the detective as "outsider," the armchair detective, a stooge narrator, involving the reader in the mystery, analytical reasoning, and applying probability to counteract conflicting evidence.

3. Perhaps no detective is more eccentric than Lieutenant Columbo! Poe's contribution to modern detective fiction is, however, much more remarkable than the introduction of these motifs or devices. Unlike all the writers of the fledgling genre that preceded him, Poe was a remarkable writer who used structure and form to create dynamic stories. Poe also stated the problem clearly and concisely, and he detailed the evidence and presented a solution based upon it.

4. Later writers capitalized on Poe's quest for the truth in his detective stories. Many, such as Arthur Conan Doyle, elevated the search for truth to the point that the discovery process became more important than the crime. His books about the eccentric detective Sherlock Holmes are a prototype for the complex process of evidence gathering. For decades, readers thought that Sherlock Holmes was a real person, and there is even a fan club devoted to him.

5. Wilkie Collins (1824-1889), a protégé of Charles Dickens, wrote *The Women in White*. Dickens is not generally known for being an author of "whodunit" novels. Called the "grandfather of English detective fiction," Collins is acclaimed for *The Moonstone*, which Dorothy L. Sayers, another popular writer of detective novels, called "probably the very finest detective story ever written." The genre, more popular than ever, continues to evolve as contemporary writers add new motifs, structure, and characteristics.

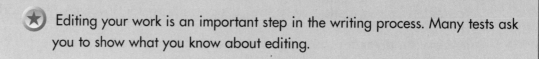

Editing Your Work

31

LITERATURE

⭐ Editing your work is an important step in the writing process. Many tests ask you to show what you know about editing.

A **Answer the questions below based on this passage.**

1) Writing teachers suggest the following guidelines for creating a detective novel or story. 2) These tips are followed by experienced writers. 3) Do not transform the detective, into the criminal. 4) Do not leave a twin or a double commit the crime, unless you prepare the reader for the existence of that twin or a double. 5) The following technique is advisable, too. 6) Writers are encouraged to make use of the "Watson" the Detective's assistant or a friend, to help reveal clues to the reader. 7) DR. Watson was Sherlock Holmes friend and colleague. 8) All clues should be known to the reader. 9) The detective uncovers critical clues through hard work, not by accident. 10) Also, the writer should not include more than one secret room or passage.

1. Identify the direct object in sentence 1.

_____

2. Rewrite sentence 2 using the active voice.

_____

_____

3. What is wrong with sentence 3?

_____

4. Correct the error in sentence 4.

_____

5. In sentence 5, what part of the sentence is *advisable*?

_____

6. Identify the capitalization and punctuation errors in sentence 6, and rewrite the sentence to correct the errors.

_____

_____

7. Identify the capitalization and punctuation errors in sentence 7, and rewrite the sentence to correct the errors.

_____

_____

8. Rewrite sentence 8 using the active voice.

_____

_____

9. Underline the direct object and the object complement in sentence 9.

10. Is sentence 10 correct? If not, why not?

_____

_____

11. What sentence can you exclude because it contains extraneous information?

_____

Name _____

Take a Test Drive

Fill in the bubble beside the correct answer.

Michael wrote a report exploring the role of setting in detective novels. Please read his work and answer the questions that follow.

The Heart and More

1) A novel's setting contains four elements. 2) That rises the question: What is "setting" if not location, geography, and physical arrangement? 3) It is intended by many authors that the time in which their novels take place be a factor in the setting. 4) Some writers leave the characters' lifestyles (such as social or economic conditions) be the most important element in setting. 5) The last element is the occupation or daily routine of the characters. 6) Setting plays a significant role in the plot and character development in Detective or—whodunit—novels.

1. Which statement is true about sentence 1?
   Ⓐ *Elements* is an indirect object.
   Ⓑ *Elements* is a direct object.
   Ⓒ *Elements* is a predicate adjective.
   Ⓓ *Elements* is a predicate nominative.

2. How should sentence 2 be changed?
   Ⓕ Change *rises* to *rose*.
   Ⓖ Change *rises* to *raised*.
   Ⓗ Change *rises* to *raises*.
   Ⓙ It is correct; no change is needed.

3. Which statement is true about sentence 3?
   Ⓐ It is written in the passive voice.
   Ⓑ It is written in the active voice.
   Ⓒ It is neither active nor passive.
   Ⓓ It is passive, then active.

4. How should sentence 4 be rewritten?
   Ⓕ Change *leave* to *lets*.   Ⓗ Change *leave* to *leaves*.
   Ⓖ Change *leave* to *leaving*.   Ⓙ Change *leave* to *let*.

5. What is true about sentence 5?
   Ⓐ It contains a direct object.
   Ⓑ It contains an indirect object.
   Ⓒ It contains a predicate nominative.
   Ⓓ It contains a predicate adjective.

6. Why does sentence 6 need to be corrected?
   Ⓕ It contains errors in capitalization.
   Ⓖ It contains errors in capitalization and punctuation.
   Ⓗ It contains errors in punctuation.
   Ⓙ It is correct; no change is needed.

During his research, Mike developed the following list of authors within two categories:
Category 1 - Classic Authors: Dashiell Hammett, Raymond Chandler, sir Arthur Conan Doyle, Ed McBain
Category 2 - Female Authors: Linda Barnes, Eleanor Taylor Bland, Lisa Cody, Janet Dawson, Janet Evanovich, Sue Grafton, Karen Kijewski, Marcia Muller, Lillian O'Donnell, Sara Paretsky, Dana Stabenow

7. What statement is false about Category 1?
   Ⓐ The authors are not listed in alphabetical order.
   Ⓑ The authors are listed in alphabetical order.
   Ⓒ The title sir should be capitalized.
   Ⓓ The authors are all male.

8. What statement is true about Category 2?
   Ⓕ The authors are not listed in alphabetical order.
   Ⓖ The authors are listed in alphabetical order.
   Ⓗ *Lillian O'Donnell* should be listed after *Janet Dawson*.
   Ⓙ *Eleanor Taylor Bland* should be listed after *Dana Stabenow*.

Here are some facts that Mike compiled while researching his report:
Police Procedurals. 1) Police procedurals written by women often take place in urban settings. 2) Characters investigate multiple crimes.
Male Private Detectives. 4) Solving more violent crimes than others. 4) Ed McBain wrote the "Mathew Hope" series. 5) Many feel protective of the client.

9. Which sentence is a fragment?
   Ⓐ sentence 4   Ⓒ sentence 5
   Ⓑ sentence 3   Ⓓ none of them

Editing for Correct Grammar

⭐ Use this checklist as a guide as you edit your work to correct grammar.

- Do you think the subject and verb agree?
- Are you using the correct tense and form of the verb?
- Is each sentence complete—not a fragment—and does it contain the appropriate punctuation and conjunctions?
- Have you placed your modifiers properly?
- Did you make a clear reference between antecedents and pronouns?
- Are any participles, infinitives, and gerunds used correctly?
- Have you misused any verbs or homophones?
- After you spell check the document, did you manually check it for usage problems that the computer didn't catch?

You may find it helpful to read your work several times—each time answering a question or two from the checklist. Many find it helpful to read the work out loud, too.

A Read the following paragraph and answer the questions.

1) Are we experienced global warming or another phase of the warming/cooling cycle of the Earth. 2) He said, An answer to that question may lay in deep ocean waters." 3) Climate is complex. 4) Land masses oceans, and the atmosphere interact to produce local climate conditions. 5) These conditions very across the globe, but conditions remain relatively stable in deep ocean water layers. 6) These layers, although stable, exert a profound effect on the globel climate system. 7) Scientists monitors these layers to reveal clues about global warming trends, if any.

1. Which sentences have punctuation errors? _____

2. Which sentence uses the wrong verb tense? _____

3. Identify the error in sentence 6. _____

4. Which sentences have incorrect word usage? _____

5. What sentence has an error in subject-verb agreement? _____

Name _____

B **Identify the errors in the following paragraph. Rewrite the paragraph to correct the errors.**

1) Studying the greenhouse effect, the earth might be 50° F coldder. 2) The atmosphere have checks and balances; but carbon dioxide, a product of industry and cars, methane, nitrous oxide, and chlorofluorocarbon molecules in the atmosphere is increasing dramatic. 3) These gases could overwhelm any natural mechanisms that might moderate the effect. 4) How does the greenhouse effect work! 5) Solar rays warm the Earth. 6) The Earth radiates infrared rays. 7) The warming rays are traped, not released, into the atmosphere.

_____

_____

_____

_____

_____

_____

_____

_____

_____

_____

_____

_____

Name _____

LESSON

Indefinite Pronouns

34

THE
CHANGING
EARTH

⭐ Pronouns and their antecedents must agree in number. A singular antecedent takes a singular pronoun, and a plural antecedent takes a plural pronoun. These indefinite pronouns take a **singular** verb:

- anybody - anything - anyone
- each - every - everybody - everything - everyone
- either - neither
- nobody - nothing - no one - not one
- one - someone - somebody - something - another
- much - many a/many an

Remember: If the indefinite pronoun comes before two or more subjects joined by and, it takes a singular verb.

These indefinite pronouns take a **plural** verb.

- both - few - many - others - several

These indefinite pronouns can be singular or plural; check the meaning of the sentence to decide.

- all - any - some - more - none

A **Underline the indefinite pronouns in the following sentences.**

1. One of the biggest areas of urban growth—the Southwest—may be built on a major weather miscalculation.

2. All depend upon the Colorado River for water.

3. Since the Hoover Dam was built in the 1930's, most are now preparing for water shortages.

4. Many experienced record growth over the last 20 years, which coincided with a 20-year wet cycle; scientists now contend that cycle was a fluke for these desert states.

5. Several are scrambling to provide water to suburbs that did not exist a generation ago.

Advantage Grammar Grade 8 © 2005 Creative Teaching Press

B **Underline the correct form of the verb to agree with the indefinite pronoun used as a subject.**

Everyone (say says) the desert will return to its normal harsh climate. The Colorado River, a source of water for cities and farms from Denver to Los Angeles, depends upon snow, but this has been the driest period in 98 years. Nobody (think thinks) the water supply is adequate, but no one (is are) addressing the problem. Someone (need needs) to take action at the federal level to encourage states to solve the problem. Marinas at Lake Powell, whose water levels are down 60 percent, are rebuilding boat ramps. Few (is are) useless already—they lead to dirt, not water!

C **Circle the phrase that agrees with the underlined antecedent.**

Some advocate for the dismantling of the Glen Canyon Dam; (he wants they want) the river to return to its natural flow. Many know what will happen when water levels continue to fall; (he knows they know) the sediments will be exposed, and weeds will soon fill the riverbed. Each state thinks (it has they have) the solution. One is filling (its their) aquifers to save for a less rainy day. Another is removing (its their) grass—an equivalent of a football field every day from public places. Others are reducing (its their) electrical power generation.

D **If the sentence is correct, mark C; if it is not correct, mark X.**

_____ 1. Some wants to take this water issue to Congress; each wants its Senator to act.

_____ 2. The Colorado River has been transformed; many an engineer marvels at its dams.

_____ 3. Others worry; they say, "have we fooled with Mother Nature too much?"

_____ 4. Past civilizations have been destroyed by drought; everyone now wonders if it will happen to their state, too.

Name _____

Placing Modifiers

⭐ Don't confuse your readers; place your modifiers properly in your sentences so your meaning is clear and easy to follow. Your modifier (whether it's a single word, clause, or phrase) should be as close as possible to the word it modifies. If you cannot move the modifier closer, consider rewriting the sentence or breaking it into two to clarify the meaning.

Tips:
- Watch placement of words such as *almost, not, nearly, only, merely,* and *simply.*
- Avoid dangling modifiers and long introductory or ending clauses and phrases. Make clear what is modified in the sentence.

A Rewrite each sentence incorporating the key word as a modifier.

Existing Sentence	Add Key Word	New Sentence
1. Sea levels have risen 560 feet since the last ice age.	nearly	
2. If all the earth's ice melted, seas would rise 230 feet.	almost	
3. Global warming over the last hundred years has caused the sea level to rise 1/16 inch a year.	almost	
4. If seas rose twenty inches in the next century, much of the Florida coastline would be submerged.	only	
5. Between 1880 and 1980, the global mean sea level rose four inches.	nearly	
6. If the Antarctic ice sheet breaks and slips into the sea, giant waves would race toward the coastal areas.	probably	

Name _____

B Write each sentence to correctly place the misplaced modifiers.

1. The student could not stop writing about the flooding in his essay.

   _____

   _____

2. The student could not stop speaking about global warming in the hallway.

   _____

   _____

3. The student could not stop asking questions about the intrusion of seawater in
   the parking lot. _____

   _____

   _____

4. The student could not stop searching for the effect of global warming on water
   supplies on the Net. _____

   _____

   _____

C Each sentence contains a misplaced modifier. Rewrite each sentence to correct it.

1. Checking the gauges every day, the ice melt was carefully tracked.

   _____

   _____

2. They liked to watch the penguins doing their checks on the gauges.

   _____

   _____

3. Without a plan for global warming, a conference seemed a good idea.

   _____

   _____

4. Fighting over a mate, the scientists were surprised by the sea lions.

   _____

   _____

Name _____

Quotation Marks

36

THE
CHANGING
EARTH

⭐ Here are some rules about the proper use of quotation marks:
- Use quotation marks at the beginning and end of the titles of poems, stories, articles, essays, songs, programs, and other short bodies of work.
- Set off expressions of slang and jargon with quotation marks.
- Set off definitions.
- Surround ironic or humorous expressions with quotation marks.
- Open and close all direct quotes with quotation marks.
- If the direct quote is just one sentence, surround the sentence with opening and closing quotation marks.
- If the direct quote is several sentences within one paragraph, place the opening quotation mark at the beginning of the direct quote and the closing quotation mark at the end of the paragraph.
- If the direct quote extends over several paragraphs, place the opening quotation mark at the beginning of each paragraph but the closing quotation mark only at the end of the last paragraph.

Here are some tips on using other marks of punctuation with quotation marks:
- Place periods and commas *inside* the *closing* quotation mark.
- Put semicolons and colons *outside* of the *closing* quotation mark.
- The placement of the question mark and exclamation mark depends upon the meaning of the sentence. If the question mark or exclamation mark applies to the entire sentence, place it outside the closing quotation mark. If the question mark or exclamation mark applies just to the quotation, place it inside the closing quotation mark.

A **If the use of quotation marks in the sentence is correct, mark the sentence with a C; if not correct, mark X.**

_____ **1.** *El Niño* is a Spanish word that means "the male child."

_____ **2.** *El Niño* is a phenomenon that the scientist called "an interplay between wind, weather, currents, and upwelling.

_____ **3.** "The *El Niño* Phenomenon" was reprinted in the school's paper.

_____ **4.** The editor said she "definitely" got permission to reprint the article.

_____ **5.** "When I called the newspaper," she added, "they said they were delighted to let us reprint it.

B Add quotation marks where needed in the following passage.

The article Understanding *El Niño* describes the phenomenon. The professor read it aloud to the student he was tutoring, It is as an oceanic event that happens around Christmas along the western coast of South America. During this event, trade winds that occur in December slack off. This, in turn, causes a decrease in the water than rises from the depths of the ocean off the coast of Peru.

Okay, then what? she asked him.

He continued, The waters become warm and nutrients die. It's the end of the peak fishing season. The impact on fisherman and entire communities can be severe, as it was during the 1982 season.

She wanted to know more, so she encouraged him to continue.

That year was the most extreme *El Niño*. Not only did the fisheries in Peru and Chile fail, but the countries of Ecuador, Peru, Paraguay, Brazil, and Argentina also experienced floods. Plus, in the middle of the Pacific Ocean, cyclones hit the islands of Tahiti and Hawaii while droughts plagued part of Africa, India, Indonesia, and Australia.

C Combine an ending punctuation mark with a closing quotation mark to end each sentence.

1. She thought a moment, then said, "But the eastern seaboard had a very warm winter

2. He was impressed and said, "Good job! Any other advantages to *El Niño*

3. "Well," she said, "I read earlier in the chapter that some warm water fish increased in number

4. Then he approached the subject from a different angle by asking, "If *El Niño* cannot be prevented, how might farmers and fisherman adjust their activities to make the most of the event? Write that down for your homework

5. After they discussed the answer, she wrote the following in her notebook, "What strategies can fisherman and farmers employ to make the most of the event? List five strategies

Name _____

Homophones

37

THE
CHANGING
EARTH

⭐ Homophones are words that sound the same but have different meanings and usually different spellings.

foreword - forward   disburse - disperse   hangar - hanger

A Look up the meanings of these homophones in your dictionary. Based on the definitions, write a clue—a few words—for each that will help you remember its meaning.

1. profit _____
   prophet _____

2. seen _____
   scene _____

3. seam _____
   seem _____

4. sheer _____
   shear _____

5. stationary _____
   stationery _____

6. taught _____
   taut _____

7. vain _____
   vane _____
   vein _____

8. weather _____
   whether _____

B Draw a line from the homophone in Column A to its "clue" meaning in Column B.

Column A	Column B
bases	military group
basis	rough
bearing	advise
baring	foundation
coarse	organization
course	baseball
core	subject
corps	to uncover
council	center
counsel	how you carry yourself

76

Name _____

C Match the words in the following list to their proper "clue" meaning in Column A; write the answers in Column B.

canvas, canvass, desert, dessert, disburse, disperse, foreword, forward, foul, fowl

Column A Clue Words	Column B Homophone
cake	
chicken	
in a book	
move	
pay	
piece of cloth	
scatter	
smelly	
survey	
leave	

D If the sentence is correct, mark *C*; if not, mark *X*. If it is incorrect, correct it.

_____ 1. Should the federal government aide the states with their water problems?

_____

_____ 2. Will watering lawns in Arizona soon be banned?

_____

_____ 3. That would be bazaar!

_____

_____ 4. Solving the water problems of western states will not be cheep.

_____

_____ 5. Should we profit from the sale of water? Should we hoard it?

_____

_____ 6. What the west needs is rein--it's not a miner problem.

_____

_____ 7. Did engineers medal too much with the Colorado?

_____

Paragraph Structure

THE
CHANGING
EARTH

⭐ Here's a blueprint for creating an effective essay.

paragraph	purpose	structure/contents
1 introductory	present thesis statement	• introductory sentences • lead-in sentences • thesis statement
2, 3, 4 body	"build a case" for the thesis statement	• lead off with transitional words, phrase, or sentence • topic sentence • sentences that "build your case" for the thesis statement
5 closing	conclude, summarize, and restate thesis statement	• lead off with transitional words, phrases, or sentence • summarize topic sentences from 2, 3, 4 • restate thesis

Here are some ways to structure your essay to "build your case" for the thesis statement:

• **Cause/Effect:** what happened first, what happened next and why; how events or relationships interact to bring about result or future result

• **Expository:** present, compare, and contrast the evidence, facts, results, and information

• **Persuasive:** give examples, facts, and evidence to present your case as to why the reader should agree or disagree

• **Descriptive:** fully render the "picture" of a person, place, thing, or idea; present all details

• **Analytical:** present, examine, and comment on evidence, facts, and information

A Here are thesis statements for student essays. Indicate which essay structure you would use to "build your case" for the statement. Write *C* for cause/effect, *E* for expository, *P* for persuasive, *D* for descriptive, and *A* for analytical.

1. Whether global warming is a reality or not, pollution from industrial waste is drastically altering air quality.

2. A subject of much discussion and exploration, polar icecaps are fascinating "players" in Earth's interdependent ecosystems.

3. Population expansion in the Asian Pacific Rim is leading to the increased clearing of mangrove swamps, which, in turn, is leading to an irreversible decline of commercial fishing.

4. Many scientists have expressed hope that the 1982 UN Convention on the Law of the Sea (UNCLOS) is the blueprint which will enable the conservation of marine ecosystems worldwide.

5. Marine Protected Areas (MPAs) encompass habitats that need protection, but there are several reasons why such protection is selective and, therefore, ineffectual.

B Select one of the thesis statements listed in exercise A above, and write the opening paragraph of an essay about it.

_____

_____

_____

_____

_____

_____

_____

Editing Your Work

 Editing your work is an important step in the writing process. Many tests ask you to show what you know about editing.

A Your teacher returned this passage to you. Rewrite it to correct all the errors she indicated.

Dr. John Harrington described the continent of Antarctica as "an unspoiled

where's the closing quotation mark?
landmass, perhaps the last on Earth. Despite this assertion, Antarctica faces

watch agreement!
severe challenges to its environment.   Few disagrees with this, but most cannot

agree with how to address its corps challenges or how to prevent damage of this

correct homophones, please.
pristine environment. Dr. Harrington is looking foreward to the debate. Bringing

should be an adverb
up the subject repeated at international conferences, the future of the continent

Be careful, You've misplaced the
may be brighter. *modifier! Rewrite.*

_____

_____

_____

_____

_____

_____

Advantage Grammar Grade 8 © 2005 Creative Teaching Press

B **Please read the passage and answer the questions below.**

1) Twenty-eight additional nations have joined the original 12 to sign the Antarctic Treaty Body. 2) Signatories have agreed to keep the Antarctic nuclear free and demilitarized. 3) Although it is devoted to research, violations do occur. 4) One protocol bands waste; all waste must be taken out, but abandoned research facilities contain garbage. 5) Building airstrips nesting sites. 6) "We cannot be complacent, the president said in his address to the international conference. 7) Few sees much chance for treaty compliance without additional legislation.

1. Write a topic sentence for this passage.

_____

2. Correct the misplaced modifier.

_____

_____

3. Find the gerund in sentence 7.

_____

4. In what sentence is a homophone used incorrectly? What word should be used?

_____

5. The subject and verb do not agree in one sentence; please identify and correct.

_____

6. Correct punctuation in sentence 6.

_____

_____

LESSON

40

THE
CHANGING
EARTH

Take a Test Drive

Fill in the bubble beside the correct answer.

1) "Was there a time when life on Earth treated oxygen as a poison, the lecturer asked, "not the life-giving substance we know it as today"? 2) Yes! 3) Although the Earth was oxygen-free a billion years ago, the amount of oxygen increased and organisms evolved to capitalize on it. 4) If we assume that anaerobic microbes were the earliest living organisms, then we can conclude that harnessing energy by degrading simple chemicals is one of the fundamental ways that organisms manufactured food. 5) In the ocean's depths, scientists talk about hydrothermal vents where chemosynthetic organisms convert hydrogen sulfide and methane into energy. 6) All agrees life soon evolved in response to a changing Earth. 7) These basic living things began to harness energy not by degrading simple chemicals but by using sunlight as energy to manufacture more complex chemicals probably. 8) The byproduct of this process was oxygen. 9) This leads us to the next evolutionary evidence.

1. If this selection was the opening paragraph for an essay, which statement is true?
   Ⓐ Sentence 3 is the topic sentence.
   Ⓑ Sentence 4 is the topic sentence.
   Ⓒ Sentence 6 is the topic sentence.
   Ⓓ Sentence 7 is the topic sentence.

2. What statement is true about sentence 5?
   Ⓕ It has a problem with subject-verb agreement.
   Ⓖ It has a misplaced modifier.
   Ⓗ It has an error in word usage.
   Ⓙ It has an error in indefinite pronoun usage.

3. What statement is false about sentence 6?
   Ⓐ It has an error in indefinite pronoun-verb agreement.
   Ⓑ It has a problem with subject-verb agreement.
   Ⓒ It is a simple sentence.
   Ⓓ It is correct as is.

4. In sentence 7, what statement is false about the word *probably*?

   Ⓕ It is a misplaced modifier.

   Ⓖ It modifies a verb.

   Ⓗ It is an adverb.

   Ⓙ It is a verb form.

5. Sentence 2 is:

   Ⓐ an error.

   Ⓑ a simple sentence.

   Ⓒ an interjection.

   Ⓓ an understood subject.

6. Which statement is true about the word *living* in sentence 4?

   Ⓕ It is a verb.

   Ⓖ It is a gerund.

   Ⓗ It is a participle.

   Ⓙ It is not used correctly.

7. Which statement is true about the role of sentence 9 in this passage?

   Ⓐ It is the topic sentence.

   Ⓑ It is the concluding sentence.

   Ⓒ It is a transitional sentence.

   Ⓓ It is a supporting sentence.

8. What statement is false about sentence 1?

   Ⓕ It is punctuated correctly.

   Ⓖ It is punctuated incorrectly.

   Ⓗ The quotation marks are needed.

   Ⓙ It is a direct quote.

9. What needs to be done in sentence 1?

   Ⓐ Place a quotation mark after the first comma.

   Ⓑ Place a quotation mark after the first comma and move the question mark inside the quotes.

   Ⓒ Move the question mark inside the quotes.

   Ⓓ Eliminate the question mark.

LESSON

41

LIFE SCIENCE

Gerunds and Gerund Phrases

⭐ Gerunds are verb forms that end in **-ing** and act as nouns. Gerunds can also be part of a phrase. Because they act as nouns, gerunds and gerund phrases can play all the roles that nouns can play including being the subject of a sentence, a direct object, and the object of preposition.

Caution: Do not confuse gerunds and gerund phrases with participial phrases! Participials and participial phrases act as adjectives and verbs, not nouns.

Participial phrase: Smashing into the earth millions of years ago, a meteor destroyed the dinosaurs.

Gerund: Scientists mourn their **passing,** but do they accept this theory?

Gerund phrase: Investigating environmental elements that contribute to extinction is not an exact science.

A **Underline the gerunds in the following sentences.**

1. Searching through records made of stone is one way to date the disappearance of dinosaurs.

2. Scientists enjoy searching the strata beds for clues to a long-ago world.

3. Some have tried tracing the extinction to other causes, such as carbon dioxide buildup from volcanic eruptions.

4. What can we learn today by studying these environmental changes of a millennium ago?

B **Identify the part of the sentence that each underlined gerund plays in Exercise A.**

1. _____

2. _____

3. _____

4. _____

C If the sentence contains a gerund or gerund phrase, mark the sentence with a *G*. If not, mark it with an *X*.

_____ **1.** Playing a critical role in the survival of species today, environmental change must be studied.

_____ **2.** Studying environmental changes is critical to the survival of species today.

_____ **3.** Changing environmental conditions will impact our survival.

_____ **4.** Changes in the climate and oceans of ages ago are being discovered by scientists.

_____ **5.** Having studied environmental changes that the earth underwent millions of years ago, scientists are revealing powerful forces at work.

_____ **6.** Are these frightening forces at work today?

_____ **7.** In correlating all the data, scientists have found that no one cause is responsible for the mass extinction of dinosaurs.

_____ **8.** The spreading of grasslands, due, in part, to the cooling of the earth, was the turning point in the history of mammals.

D Convert the verbs to gerunds and write a sentence using the gerund as the part of the sentence indicated.

<u>verb</u>   <u>part of sentence</u>

1. study   subject _____

_____

_____

2. analyze   object of preposition _____

_____

_____

3. drive   direct object _____

_____

Name _____

Coordinating Conjunctions

⭐ The coordinating conjunctions—**and, but, or, nor**—are used to join independent clauses as well as phrases and words of equal rank.

> The mass extinctions all began with global temperature change **and** a large drop in sea level.

When using a coordinating conjunction to connect two or more items in a series, use a comma between the items and before the conjunction.

> After ice sheets spread across **North America, Europe, and Asia**, a mile of ice covered nearly one-third of those continents. How did early man adapt?

Connect two independent clauses with coordinating conjunctions and the proper punctuation.

> The Earth underwent major changes in climate, **and** early man adapted by migrating to more life-sustaining environments.

A Insert commas where needed in the following sentences. If the sentence does not need a comma, mark it with an *X*.

_____ 1. Two-thirds of North and South America's large mammals disappeared over the course of a thousand years, nearly 11,000 years ago.

_____ 2. They fell victim to millions of years of extreme conditions climate changes and unstable ecosystems.

_____ 3. Is it any coincidence that the arrival of man coincided with this great extinction and is there growing evidence that man helped to hasten this great extinction of Ice Age mammals?

_____ 4. The Overkill Hypothesis is controversial highly charged and emotional.

_____ 5. Could man have killed the majority of "big game" with Stone Age technology and destroyed so many large mammals within a single millennium of arriving in North America?

B **Using the appropriate coordinating conjunction, link the two sentences to make one logical sentence.**

1. An "endangered" species is one that will become extinct within the foreseeable future. A "threatened" species is one that is likely to become endangered within the foreseeable future. _____

   _____

   _____

   _____

   _____

2. The World Conservation Union listed 5,205 animal species as either "critically endangered" or "vulnerable to extinction" in its 1996 report of threatened animals. This represented a huge increase in just six years. _____

   _____

   _____

   _____

   _____

   _____

3. Nine billion passenger pigeons filled the skies in 1850. they were slaughtered by the millions for food and target practice. _____

   _____

   _____

   _____

   _____

4. The New York Zoological Society, the National Zoo, private reserves, and the Cincinnati Zoo rescued the American bison from a similar fate. It, too, would not have survived to bear witness to our national heritage. _____

   _____

   _____

   _____

   _____

   _____

Name _____

Compound and Compound-Complex Sentences

⭐ An **independent clause** always contains a subject and a verb, and it can stand on its own. A **dependent clause** *may* contain a subject and a verb, but it cannot stand on its own.

A **compound sentence** has at least two independent clauses joined by either a coordinating conjunction with a comma or by a semicolon.

A **compound-complex** sentence has at least two independent clauses (joined by either a coordinating conjunction with a comma or by a semicolon) and one or more dependent clauses.

Remember: After you have separated independent clauses with punctuation, add punctuation, if any, for your dependent clauses.

A Underline the independent clauses in the following compound sentences.

1. Twenty colonizing species developed into the entire bird population of Hawaii, and many of the species they evolved into became flightless.

2. The flightless birds fell victim to humans and habitation destruction, but scientists have found clear evidence of them in fossil records.

3. Since the arrival of Captain Cook in the Hawaiian Islands in 1778, 16 bird species have been lost, and 24 are listed as rare or endangered.

B Underline the dependent clauses in the following compound-complex sentences.

1. Hawaii's colonizing bird species, which arrived by flight from lands far away, diversified quite rapidly into new species, and none of them had to worry about predators.

2. When hungry humans arrived on the islands of Hawaii, they brought dogs with them; the flightless birds were soon in fear for their lives.

3. These birds, which had once been waterfowl, walked and waddled, but they did not fly.

C **Punctuate the following compound and compound-complex sentences with commas and semicolons as needed.**

1. The feathered caps of Hawaiian kings and queens each required the feathers of 80,000 birds the preparation of these caps alone must have resulted in the extinction of species.

2. Throughout Hawaii on street corners in schools and near public buildings you will find signs bearing a likeness of a Hawaiian king wearing a cap of pink feathers is it a surprise that only nine native bird fauna remain from the hundreds that existed before humans arrived?

3. Scientists around the world are finding excavating and studying bird fossils they are also discovering a pattern that links the arrival of man with the extinction of native species.

D **From the following research notes, create a new paragraph that contains compound and compound-complex sentences.**

Scientists argue. Some say, since Ice Age, extinctions are not important. Percent of species becoming extinct now = a fraction of the total number on the earth. Others say the number of extinctions in the last million years = more than when the dinosaurs dissappeared. Hawaii—one thousand bird species and one thousand snail species disappeared.

_____

_____

_____

_____

_____

_____

_____

_____

LESSON

44

LIFE SCIENCE

Using Apostrophes

⭐ Contractions such as *don't* and *isn't* contain apostrophes. This versatile punctuation mark can also be use to designate:

- **a quotation within a quotation:** Dr. Brown said, "When I first learned of the study, I thought of the words, **'struck by lighting,'** to describe how I felt."

- **an omission of figures in date:** the Olympic Games of **'04**, the class of **'10**, in the **'90s**

- **the measurement of feet:** an excavation plot **15' x 30'**

Apostrophes are also used to form possessive nouns and pronouns. Use the apostrophe before the *s* if the word is singular. Place the apostrophe after the *s* if it is plural.

singular Dr. **Ehlich's** work is celebrated at Stanford University.
The contributions of Stanford **University's** professors are celebrated worldwide.
"Those poor results are **someone's** fault," she said, "but not mine."
Your **boss's** approval can translate into a bonus for you.
The **stockholder's** claim that he was cheated was proven false.

plural The **students'** reports have improved.
The contributions of public **universities'** professors are undervalued worldwide.
Women's contributions to the study of genetics are often overlooked.
The **stockholders'** claim that they were cheated was proven false.

A **Abbreviate the dates in the following sentences:**

1. He graduated from college in 1999 with a degree in genetic engineering, but she studied for a graduate degree in paleontology from 1997 to 2003.

2. In the 1970s, the United States passed an important law to help preserve species, and in 1977, regulations under the Convention on International Trade in Endangered Species of Wild Fauna and Flora (CITES) took effect.

3. The American bald eagle was listed as endangered in 43 states in 1978.

B **Punctuate the quotations in the following sentences.**

1. The scientist expressed himself clearly when he said, We want to remember the words, We have nothing to fear, but fear itself, as we undertake this important mission.

2. He ended his remarks with, The results show which traits are inherited and which come from the environment—or as Dr. Johnson said, are derived from environmental constructs—and are published in this report.

3. The student said, I copied her inspiring words on the cover of my notebook, Do the best you can.

C **Add apostrophes to the measurements in the following sentences.**

1. The scientists studied the fossil which measured approximately 8 x 10.

2. The fossil of a dinosaur 5 high by 10 long was compressed into a space measuring 3 square.

3. How many cubic yards are dirt are in a plot which measures 13 x 26?

D **If the possessives in the following sentences are formed correctly, mark _C_; if not, mark _X_.**

_____ 1. Dr. Brays position is clear.

_____ 2. The American Zoo and Aquarium Associations "Species Survival Plan" in 1999 protected 67 mammals.

_____ 3. What was Harvard biologist Edward Wilson's famous remark?

_____ 4. In Niles Eldredge's 1998 book, it was reported that 30,000 plant and animal species are lost each year.

_____ 5. For him, paleontology was a hobby; then, this do-it-yourselfer's obsession turned into a career.

Name _____

⭐ Double the final consonant of a word before you add a suffix:
- When the word ends in a vowel-consonant combination.
    sw<u>im</u> - swimmer   st<u>op</u> - stopping
- When the last syllable of the verb receives the accent.
    ad<u>mit</u> - admitting
- When the suffix to be added starts with a vowel.
    control + <u>er</u> = controller

Exceptions:
- Do not double the final consonant if it is a **y, s, w,** or **x**.
    toy - toying   bus - buses   sew - sewing   tax - taxed
- Do not double the final consonant if the accent shifts from the final syllable.
    refer - reference

A If the word is spelled correctly, mark a *C*; if not, mark *X*.

_____ 1. equalled

_____ 2. quiting

_____ 3. jinxxed

_____ 4. mugy

_____ 5. wishful

_____ 6. fully

_____ 7. preferred

_____ 8. concurent

_____ 9. regrettable

_____ 10. displaying

B Circle the correct spelling.

1.	gleamming	gleaming
2.	defered	deferred
3.	getting	geting
4.	conferring	confering
5.	folded	foldded
6.	biten	bitten
7.	severly	severely
8.	retained	retainned
9.	taxxing	taxing
10.	swaged	swagged

Name _____

C Add the suffix to the following words, doubling final consonant as needed, to make a new word.

original word	suffix	new word
1. artful	ly	
2. bat	ing	
3. bloom	er	
4. bud	ed	
5. can	ed	
6. clip	ed	
7. control	ing	
8. fulfill	ing	
9. infer	ed	
10. infer	ence	
11. mar	ing	
12. mop	ed	
13. refer	ence	
14. transfer	ee	
15. tag	ed	

D Add either the suffixes *ing* or *ed* to each word.

1. swat _____   6. omit _____

2. fit _____   7. equip _____

3. handicap _____   8. flat _____

4. benefit _____   9. excel _____

5. ski _____   10. clap _____

LESSON

46

LIFE SCIENCE

Logical Sequence

Paragraphs are driven by topic sentences. All other sentences in a paragraph elaborate on, explain, detail, prove, or define that topic sentence. It is important to sequence the sentences in a paragraph logically. In doing so, you help your reader understand your message.

A **Number the sentences to create a logical sequence for a paragraph. Number 1 should be your topic sentence.**

_____ **a.** There are about 4,500 species of mammals on Earth today; a typical species survives for about a million years.

_____ **b.** Although humans depend upon the diversity of life for survival, our actions and resource demands are speeding up the extinction of mammal species.

_____ **c.** For example, between 1600 and 1810, 38 species were lost as compared with 112 species between 1810 and 1994.

_____ **d.** Sadly, 20 mammal species have become extinct since 1990.

_____ **e.** Therefore, scientists expect that one species should become extinct about every 225 years, but the rate is actually much higher.

B **Select the topic sentence for a paragraph about threatened wildlife which will discuss the following facts.**

1. _____

- global warming
- pollution
- habitation destruction
- population growth

a) Water quality is a key to improving health.
b) Humans are living longer than ever before.
c) Our quality of life is worse now than ever before.
d) Several environmental factors are affecting the survival of species.

C Write a topic sentence for each group of facts.

1. _____

   _____

   _____

   - climate change alters habitats
   - deforestation leads to loss of soil nutrients
   - fire destroys shelter and food supply
   - non-native predator species kill native species

2. _____

   _____

   _____

   - we inherit genes from parents
   - we are born with certain abilities
   - we learn by copying others
   - we grow and change as we mature

D Write a paragraph of you own with a topic sentence and several supporitng sentences.

_____

_____

_____

_____

_____

_____

_____

_____

_____

Name _____

Editing Your Work

 Editing your work is an important step in the writing process. Many tests ask you to show what you know about editing.

A **Nat wrote a paper for science class about the Human Genome Project. Here is part of what he wrote. Read Nat's paragraph and answer the questions that follow to help him edit it.**

1) Early in the 90s, scientists set out to do something that had never been done before. 2) The identification of all the genes in human DNA became the goal of the Human Genome Project. 3) Completed in 2003, the project was coordinated by the U.S. Department of Energy and the National Institutes of Health; the Wellcome Trust from the United Kingdom was a major partner and additional contributions came from Japan France Germany China and others

1. Punctuate the date in sentence 1. _____

2. Rewrite sentence 2 changing *The identification of* into a gerund.

_____

_____

3. List the four clauses in sentence 3 and tell whether each is dependent or independent. Add commas where they are needed.

_____

_____

_____

_____

_____

_____

_____

B **Continue reading and correcting Nat's report.**

1) Although the HGP is now finished, scientists will be analyzing the data for many years to come. 2) There is much to be learned. 3) For example, the study of genes will help us learn about the common biology that all life shares. 4) Comparring human genes with those of other organisms will help scientists identify genes that are associated with specific diseases and traits.

5) Will scientists discover a gene that stops aging? 6) Can scientists engineer a gene to reverse or arrest cancer by the year 2010? 7) The new discoveries that scientists will find in the future will challenge our world.

1. What part of speech is the word *analyzing* in sentence 1?

_____

2. Rewrite sentence 3 so that it includes a gerund.

_____

_____

3. Identify the spelling error in sentence 4. Write the word correctly on the lne below.

_____

4. Rewrite sentences 3 and 4 so that they are a compound sentence.

_____

_____

_____

_____

5. In sentence 6, change *engineer* to a gerund and rewrite the sentence so that the gerund is the subject.

_____

_____

_____

6. Write a good topic sentence to begin the second paragraph.

_____

_____

_____

Name _____

Fill in the bubble beside the correct answer.

Nature or Nurture?

1) What has more impact on our health and how long we live, nature or nurture? 2) Nature refers to your genes and biology; nurture refers to how you were brought up. 3) Scientists have debated this topic for years, but the discoveries of the Human Genome Project may support the argument that nurture (environmental factors) has the upper hand. 4) Scientists found that humans have 30,000 genes, only slightly more genes than a fruit fly! 5) Craig Venter of the company Celera Genomics was a member of one of the two teams that cracked the human genome. 6) Venter has been quoted as saying, "We simply do not have enough genes for this idea of biological determinism to be right." *Biological determinism* means that you were programmed by your DNA and genes to behave in a certain way.

1. If this selection is the opening paragraph for an essay, which statement is true?
Ⓐ Sentence 2 is the topic sentence.
Ⓑ Sentence 3 is the topic sentence.
Ⓒ Sentence 4 is the topic sentence.
Ⓓ Sentence 5 is the topic sentence.

2. What statement is true about sentence 3?
Ⓕ It is a sentence fragment.
Ⓖ It is a simple sentence.
Ⓗ It is a compound sentence.
Ⓙ It is a compound-complex sentence.

3. What statement is false about *upper* in sentence 3?
Ⓐ It is an adjective.
Ⓑ It is spelled correctly.
Ⓒ It is spelled incorrectly.
Ⓓ It modifies *hand*.

1) Venter and others are exploring the idea that cancers are largely caused by environmental rather than inherited factors. 2) No one is dismissing heredity's role just yet, however; others expect that more genes will be discovered over time. 3) In fact, human genes produce many related proteins capable of performing different functions. 4) One estimate is that our 30,000 genes make ten times as many proteins. 5) Scientists have decades of work to do to discover what functions these proteins play. 6) Also, DNA contains "snips," sites that vary between unrelated individuals. 7) Do "snips" have consequences for our health and well-being? 8) Researchers are just beginning to investigate what those consequences, if any, might be.

4. In sentence 3, what statement is false about *performing*?
- Ⓕ It is a gerund.
- Ⓖ It is an object of a preposition.
- Ⓗ It is a verb.
- Ⓙ It is an abverb.

5. Sentence 2 is a:
- Ⓐ sentence fragment.
- Ⓑ simple sentence.
- Ⓒ compound sentence.
- Ⓓ compound-complex sentence.

1) These are fascinating examples of the interaction between heredity and environment. 2) The Human Genome Project has sparked a debate about what role genes play in shaping behavior and personality. 3) Scientists and researchers are exploring whether single genes have a major impact on behavior. 4) Discovering genes that control such behaviors as shyness have provided clues to the answer. 5) They suspect that proteins from our genes have a dramatic effect on personali-ties, and moods. 6) But most geneticists acknowledge that the environment also plays a major role in shaping behavior, temperament, and intelligence.

6. Which statement is true about *discovering* in sentence 4?
- Ⓕ It is a verb.
- Ⓖ It is a gerund.
- Ⓗ It is a participle.
- Ⓙ It is not used correctly.

7. Which statement is true about Sentence 1?
- Ⓐ Sentence 1 is the topic sentence of the paragraph
- Ⓑ Sentence 1 does not belong in this paragraph.
- Ⓒ Sentence 1 is the introduction to the paragraph.
- Ⓓ Sentence 1 contains a misspelled word.

Practice Test

One of your classmates prepared an essay about El Niño. Here's the first paragraph and part of the second. Read it and answer the questions that follow.

1) El Niño, the weather phenomenon caused by the interplay of wind, warm water, and ocean currents in the Pacific Ocean, has played a major role in history. 2) In 1588, the Spanish Armada, which ruled the seas and helped the Spanish Empire conquer the world, was destroyed by a severe storm. 3) Was El Niño to blame? 4) More than 40 million deaths in 1877 from drought in India and China can be attributed to El Niño. 5) Can Hitler's defeat on the Russian front during the cruel winter of 1942 also be blamed on El Niño? 6) "After the 1997 El Niño, $20 billion in damages were accrued worldwide, one agency reported.

7) To help counteract the devastating effects of this weather phenomenon, scientists are trying to perfect their ability to predict El Niño.

1. Which is the topic sentence of the first paragraph?

Ⓐ sentence 1

Ⓑ sentence 2

Ⓒ sentence 3

Ⓓ sentence 4

2. Which sentence could logically follow sentence 7?

Ⓕ Scientists only have a window of a few years to test their predictions.

Ⓖ Climate research takes time.

Ⓗ Early in 2004, researchers at Columbia University claimed they developed a way to predict El Niño up to two years in advance.

Ⓙ They forecasted a wet winter in the southern United States.

3. Based on this opening paragraph, what type of essay will this be?

Ⓐ cause/effect

Ⓑ expository

Ⓒ persuasive

Ⓓ analytical

4. Which transitional word or phrase could be added to the beginning of sentence 4?

   Ⓕ in addition

   Ⓖ consequently

   Ⓗ without a doubt

   Ⓙ as a result

5. Which change to sentence 1 is best?

   Ⓐ Playing a major role in history, caused by the interplay of wind, warm water, and ocean currents; El Niño, the weather phenomenon, is in the Pacific Ocean.

   Ⓑ El Niño, as a weather phenomenon, is caused by the interplay of wind, warm water, and ocean currents in the Pacific Ocean; and has played a major role in history.

   Ⓒ What weather phenomenon caused by the interplay of wind, warm water, and ocean currents in the Pacific Ocean has played a major role in history?

   Ⓓ The weather phenomenon El Niño is caused by the interplay of wind, warm water, and ocean currents in the Pacific Ocean; it has played a major role in history.

6. Which word is spelled correctly?

   Ⓕ conquerred

   Ⓖ causeing

   Ⓗ counteracting

   Ⓙ perfectted

7. What change, if any, should be made in sentence 6?

   Ⓐ add quotation mark after the second comma

   Ⓑ eliminate quotation mark at beginning of sentence

   Ⓒ add quotation mark after period

   Ⓓ no change needed

Practice Test

Another student submitted this additional information about El Niño. Read this passage and answer the questions that follow.

1) Occurring every two to seven years, El Niño develops in April, May, June; then, it seems to peak between December and February. 2) Although scientists have documented the phenomenon's effect on climate, they are just beginning to examine its roll in health. 3) Death due to drought and flood brought on by El Niño was well documented in 97 by scientists. 4) Yes, disease outbreaks can be triggered by extreme weather. 5) All hopes to develop data which, when analyzed, will help public health officials control future epidemics or prevent public health disasters caused by El Niño. 6) Exploring scientific evidence and national data is key to reaching that goal. 7) Mindful that other facts (such as immunity) impact disease transmission, infectious diseases such as mosquito- and rodent-born diseases are being explored. 8) Scientists and researchers are ready to make suggestions. 9) Either their report or their advise are due soon. 10) Preliminary analysis, however, has already appeared in journals.

8. **Exploring** in sentence 6 is:
   Ⓐ a verb
   Ⓑ a gerund
   Ⓒ a participle
   Ⓓ an infinite

9. What is true about sentence 7?
   Ⓕ It has a problem with subject-verb agreement.
   Ⓖ It has a misplaced modifier.
   Ⓗ It has an error in word usage.
   Ⓙ It is correct as is.

10. What change, if any, should be made in sentence 1?
   Ⓐ change **seems** to **seams**
   Ⓑ eliminate semicolon
   Ⓒ add **and** after third comma
   Ⓓ add **and** before semicolon

Advantage Grammar Grade 8 © 2005 Creative Teaching Press

11. What change, if any, should be made in sentence 2?
- Ⓕ change just to only
- Ⓖ change documented to documenting
- Ⓗ change roll to role
- Ⓙ no change needed

12. **Occurring** in sentence 1 is:
- Ⓐ a verb
- Ⓑ a gerund
- Ⓒ a participle
- Ⓓ an infinitive

13. What change, if any, should be made to sentence 3?
- Ⓕ change 97 to '97
- Ⓖ change **well** to **good**
- Ⓗ change **due** to **do**
- Ⓙ no change needed

14. In sentence 4, **Yes** is what part of speech?
- Ⓐ noun
- Ⓑ adjective
- Ⓒ preposition
- Ⓓ interjection

15. In sentence 5, what change, if any, should be made?
- Ⓕ change **hopes** to **hoping**
- Ⓖ change **hopes** to **hopping**
- Ⓗ change **hopes** to **hope**
- Ⓙ no change needed

16. Which is true about sentence 9?
- Ⓐ The verb is correct.
- Ⓑ It contains a gerund.
- Ⓒ It has two errors.
- Ⓓ It is correct.

Answer Key

Lesson 1

A Students must draw a line to:
1. Franklin
2. Franklin, ideas
3. Franklin

B
1. It was **exhausting** work.
2. The **exhausted** delegates kept working.
3. It was **surprising** news.

C
1. thriving
2. excited
3. thrilled
4. presiding
5. interesting
6. fascinating, respected

D
1. Challenging all of us, Franklin's words awed us.

Lesson 2

A
1. were
2. explain
3. play
4. need
5. expresses
6. prompt
7. set
8. predicts/speaks
9. taint
10. were

B Sentences may vary, but verbs are:
1. promotes
2. travel
3. believe
4. drafts
5. destroys

Lesson 3

A Answers will vary, but should approximate the content shown here.
1. Why was Benjamin Franklin's image chosen to be on the $100 bill?
2. This founding father signed all three major documents that helped free the colonies from British rule: the Declaration of Independence, the Treaty of Paris, and the United States Constitution.
3. This man defined "good citizenship"!
4. He is also credited with founding or helping to form numerous organizations and institutions such as hospitals, libraries, and insurance companies. He was driven by a strong sense of civic duty.

B
1. revised it
2. signed - representatives
3. 81, in frail health, but intellectually alert

Lesson 4

A
1. John Adams, along with his cousin Samuel Adams, helped to secure the appointment of George Washington as commander of the new army.
2. Was Adams sixty-two when he became president?
3. Before becoming our second president, Adams served as our country's first vice president (1789-1797).
4. Abigail Adams' letters—witty, vivid, and written just as she spoke—tell the story of a woman who struggled with the hardship of war.
5. As a First Lady, Adams fulfilled her duties willingly—even in the primitive conditions in the new capital of Washington, D.C., in 1800.

B

	Student 1	Student 2
1.	wrong	correct
2.	correct	wrong
3.	correct	correct
4.	correct	wrong
5.	wrong	correct
6.	wrong	correct

Lesson 5

A
1. devised
2. ensured
3. incite
4. envelopes
5. advise
6. discreet
7. capital, legislators
8. guess
9. compliment

B
1. X
2. C
3. C
4. C
5. X
6. X
7. X
8. C
9. C

Lesson 6

A
1. 5, 8
2. 13
3. In that role, he was able to negotiate an alliance between France and the colonies.
4. 11
5. One of his most significant contributions was in the diplomatic arena.
6. **Prowess** means "superior ability and skill" or "bravery and valor." It is used correctly in sentence 12.
7. spelling error—**hour** should be **our**
8. The fourth paragraph credits the work of Adams and Jay, but no mention is made in the third paragraph what that work was or how they were involved.

Lesson 7

A
1. (1706:1790) should be (1706-1790)
2. answer will vary
3. His publications as well as his experience **are** diversified.
4. publish-er or pub-lisher
5. no—change **respecting** to **respected**
6. incorrect subject-verb agreement—change **credit** to **credits**
7. device

Advantage Grammar Grade 8 © 2005 Creative Teaching Press

8. opposing
9. **believe** should be **believing**
10. advice

Lesson 8
A
1. A   6. G
2. G   7. B
3. B   8. H
4. H   9. B
5. C

Lesson 9
A
1. Missouri Compromise
2. secession crisis
3. Lee, Grant, Jackson, and Sherman
4. Robert E. Lee

B
1. their
2. itself
3. it
4. they

C
1. their
2. she
3. her

D
1. The victorious general was elated, but he kept his elation contained.
2. The new forms arrived late. The generals wanted the soldiers to surrender, not attack.

Lesson 10
A
1. shortest
2. most inspiring
3. closer
4. smartest

B
1. change **better** to **best**
2. change **tallest** to **taller**
3. change **more** to **most**
4. change **best** to **better**

C
1. most difficult
2. slowest
3. valuable
4. sillier
5. happier
6. worst

Lesson 11
A
1. d
2. c
3. b

B Answers may vary.

Lesson 12
A
1. C   6. C
2. C   7. X
3. C   8. C
4. X   9. X
5. X

B
1. X   3. X
2. X   4. X

Lesson 13
A
1. troops   7. women's
2. principle   8. secede
3. preceded   9. proffered
4. principal   10. woman's, thorough
5. unconscious   11. tenet
6. troops   12. prefer

B
1. troupe   6. unconscientious
2. prefer   7. succeed (or proceed)
3. woman's   8. principle
4. proceed   9. tenet
5. thorough

Lesson 14
A.
1. underline **after all that's said and done**
2. most
3. change **it** to **they**
4. One former slave said, "50 to 100 lashes with a whip was regular punishment."
5. slave owners encouraged some slaves
6. How many families were disrupted?
7. Slave owners ended as many as one-third of slave marriages.
8. answer can vary
9. change **best** to **better**
10. 70
11. underline **educating**

Lesson 15
A
1. underline **no sooner**
   Once we finished studying the Revolutionary War, we started to read about the Civil War.
2. underline **principle** and **succeeding**
   First, we studied the roots of the war, including the principal reason for states seceding.
3. The bracket should be replaced by a parenthesis.
4. We studied his biography, read his speeches, and reviewed his policies.
5. The sentence is correct.
6. Circle **their** because the pronoun **his** is needed to modify **each man**. The pronoun must agree in number with its antecedent.

B

Most slaves were severely punished for disobeying their owners or trying to escape. Nat Turner was one slave who tried to revolt against slavery. His efforts failed. He was enslaved in Virginia, and he was also a preacher to his people. At first, seven slaves joined the revolt (1831); but over the next two days, they were soon joined by 75 other slaves. Turner's owner, Joseph Travis, and his family were killed, and a total of 50 white people were murdered. Six weeks later, Turner was captured and hanged, and the revolt was put down by a troop of 3,000 citizens.

Lesson 16

1. D
2. G
3. A
4. G
5. D
6. H
7. A

Lesson 17
A

1. noun-verb-conjunction
2. verb-preposition
3. interjection
4. verb-adjective - adverb
5. pronoun
6. pronoun-verb-noun

B

1. Teachers spend hours fighting deception, and some read everything with a cynical eye.
2. change **easy** to **easily**
3. adjective
4. adverb-eagerly adjective-computerized
5. delete **first**
6. change **quick** to **quickly**   Services like these not only provide teachers with detailed reports about sections of text copied verbatim from the Internet, but they also quickly provide the link to the sources.
7. adjective
8. to
9. yes
10. districts, companies

Lesson 18
A

1. AOL, <u>which you can subscribe to</u>, is one of the largest Internet Services Providers.
2. <u>If you want a community experience</u>, you can join AOL or any other large ISP.
3. A screen name, <u>which your ISP enables you to select</u>, identifies you online.
4. You can use a number of screen names <u>when you search the Web.</u>
5. Some screen names are obvious, but some do not make sense <u>until you examine them closer.</u>

B

1. D
2. X
3. D
4. D

C

Answers will vary.

D

1. ADJ
2. ADV
3. N
4. N

Lesson 19
A

1. One blogger, <u>a lawyer</u>, uses his blog to comment on legal cases and issues of law.
2. The pioneering blogger, <u>a Harvard fellow and founder of successful technology companies</u>, presented a conference on blogging.
3. Dan Gillmore, <u>a San Jose Mercury News columnist</u>, has a blog.
4. <u>A grassroots movement</u>, blogging is not yet being embraced by business, although some are becoming converts.
5. One chief technology officer, <u>a prolific Web surfer</u>, has traded frequent emails for blogging.

B

1. N
2. E
3. E
4. E
5. N
6. N
7. N
8. N

C

After 9-11-01, some New Yorkers who lived and worked around the World Trade Center kept online journals to relate their experiences. These blogs drew millions of readers because they were eyewitness accounts. You, too, can keep a blog, if you are interested. When you build your blog, however, you should not expect millions of readers! In fact, readers will not return to your blog unless you keep it current.

There are many technical tools that you can access to build and maintain your blog, if you find the time to devote to blogging. Unless your research indicates otherwise, you can keep your blog fairly simple. There are three types of blogs—microjournal, notebook, and filter; and you can start one with the help of a blogging service provider, which helps you can create a blog account in minutes. If you have the confidence and the ability, you can also create a blog with software, which gives you options to use movable type, link to other sites, search, and index.

Lesson 20
A

1. What causes someone to start a hoax on the Net: boredom, stupidity, or evil intent?
2. The Securities and Exchange Commission, which is worried about stock manipulation online, has investigated and charged many who have posted bogus press releases about corporate earnings.
3. A Net rumor about dihydrogen monoxide, commonly known as water, caused a city in California to panic and pass a law banning materials made with the substance!

B

1. One persistent hoax alerted people to a proposed E-mail tax; another claimed that Honda was giving away free cars.
2. Some hoaxes mask viruses; consume space within your mailbox, causing you the inconvenience and time to shift through E-mail; and spread fear.
3. You may have received a hoax convincing you to delete a necessary operating file, claiming it was a virus; to send money; or to submit personal information, claiming you have won a prize.
4. Sites such as truthorfiction.com, snopes.com, and hoaxbusters.ciac.org can help you be a hoax-buster; you can even refer to symantec.com/avcenter/hoax.html or vil.mcafee.com/hoax.asp to verify virus hoaxes.

C

Internet hoaxes fall into different categories. One preys on emotions. An emotional appeal on behalf of a child dying of cancer asked people to donate money and wanted them to forward the E-mail to friends. Another appeals to greed. One company's stock soared when an Internet rumor was spread about a corporate takeover and fell when it denied the rumor. Some of these greed-based appeals bilk people out of money, take their personal information, and trick them into surrendering passwords. Some hoaxes capitalize on people's desires for good deals. Take, for example, the hoax that Disney World, Microsoft, and The Gap would reward people for forwarding email to their friends. These companies do not track our email, but focus on their real business.

Lesson 21

A

agri-field	dogma-opinion
ambul-walk	form-shape
aqua-water	ques-ask
biblio-book	tain-hold
cycl-circle	therm-heat

B

Answer may vary, but it should approximate those listed here.

C

Answer may vary, but several samples are shown here.

revolve	terrain
vacuum	tortious
urban	construct
telescope	phonics
terminate	sanitary

D

cam
cap
ceed
cert

Lesson 22

A

"Without a doubt, I need a guide to cyberspace," said Drew's father in frustration when he subscribed to an Internet Service Provider. Before long, Drew found just the thing his father needed—a book called *The Young Surfer's Guide to Cyberspace*. Before Drew could even show him the chapters in the book, his father protested, "But that's for kids!" As a result, Drew explained just how much the book had helped him when he received it for a birthday present. He pointed out how it saved hours of time. For example, he learned about newsgroups and found great information for school reports. Otherwise, he would have spent hours going to the library looking for the same detail. "Okay, I'll take a look," his dad said finally. "Looks like I need help."

B

Answers will vary.

C

Answer may vary, but they should resemble:

Before homework, I visit the "Photo and Arts" section at nationalgeographic.com/education/homework. The site challenges me to guess what a photo is. Clues in a scrolling box help me identify the photographs. In addition, I can check my answers. For homework help, however, I search the other sections, in particular, "History" and "Science."

Lesson 23

A

1. For example, many people receive bogus messages regarding a new virus.
   Another example of Internet abuse is music piracy.
2. today - increasingly
3. verbs
4. first
5. adjective - theft
6. which represents major music companies - nonessential
7. Instead of copying another's work word-for-word, students can learn to paraphrase the material, attribute the material with quotations, acknowledge the original author, or comment on the original work.
8. add comma after **computer** and **connections**—to set off a dependent clause
9. add a comma after **quotations**—a series needs to be separate by a comma
10. add a semicolon after **helpful**
11. dismissed—exception

Lesson 24

1.	A	6.	H
2.	H	7.	B
3.	B	8.	H
4.	G	9.	C
5.	A	10.	J

Answer Key

Lesson 25
A
1. PN
2. PN
3. DO
4. DO
5. DO
6. PN
7. IO
8. PA
9. PN
10. OC

B
1. Hammett's writing was <u>spare</u>, and his style influenced diverse <u>writers</u>.
2. Before Hammett, most mysteries were <u>romantic</u>.
3. The urban settings for his novels seemed <u>realistic</u> and <u>gritty</u>.
4. His detectives are isolated <u>men</u>.
5. He presented a violent <u>view</u> of American society.

Lesson 26
A
1. go - leave
2. take - let - set
3. rose - left
4. raises
5. lying

B
"How can I convince the jury of that!" The lawyer did not believe his client, and he could not let this meeting end without being sure. After the meeting, he had to <u>come</u> [go] to courtroom and defend the man, but he still needed evidence he could <u>bring</u> [take] to the jury. He <u>raised</u> [rose] from his chair and went to the window.

"What's the problem?" the client asked.

"<u>Go</u> [come] with me," the lawyer said suddenly. He turned away from the window and picked up his briefcase that was <u>laying</u> [lying] on the desk.

The client rose up, but then <u>set</u> [sat] right down again. "Hey, I have to <u>rise</u> [raise] a point," he said.

"There's no time," the lawyer said, <u>lying</u> [laying] his hand on the doorknob.

"Well, you cannot <u>come</u> [go] back to that courtroom without me, can you?"

"You <u>rise</u> [raise] a good point," the lawyer said, sitting down again.

Lesson 27
A
Answers my vary.
1) The amateur sleuth Nancy Drew was the heroine of a popular detective series.
2) Anonymous authors wrote the books that were published under the pseudonym Carolyn Keene.
3) Mildred Wirt Benson wrote many of the books early in the series.
4) Stratemeyer Syndicate sold more than 200 million copies of the Nancy Drew series worldwide.
5) no change
6) no change
7) no change
8) The characters George Fayne and Bess Marvin were her close friends, and her boyfriend Ned Nickerson also lent his support.

B
Answers will vary.

Lesson 28
A
1. X
2. X
3. C
4. X
5. X
6. C
7. X
8. X
9. X
10. C

B
1. Edgar Allan Poe is the father of modern "whodunit" novels in the detective genre.
2. His story, "The Tell-Tale Heart," presents a genuine mystery.
3. To this day, critics debate the solution of the mystery: What did the murderer hear?
4. The murderer was also the first-person narrator of the story.
5. Was it midnight or 3 A.M. when he visited the old man's room?
6. For days after he killed the old man, the murderer was tortured by a hideous sound.
7. He believed he heard the dead man's heart beating.

C
Answers will vary.

Lesson 29
A
Raymond Chandler, Ms. Leslie Charteris, G. K. Chesterton, Agatha Christie, Patricia Cornwell, Ms. Amanda Cross

B
99 Steps, The Scarlet Slipper Mystery, A Secret at Shadow Ranch, The Secret of the Old Clock, The Sign of the Twisted Candles, Strange Message in the Parchment

Lesson 30
A
1. Many fictional accounts have been written about the real-life criminal Jack the Ripper.
2. Not much is known about his personal life, however.
3. Perhaps no detective is more eccentric than Lieutenant Columbo!
4. For decades, readers thought that Sherlock Holmes was a real person, and there is even a fan club devoted to him.
5. Dickens is not generally known for being an author of "whodunit" novels.

Lesson 31
A
1. guidelines
2. Experienced writers follow these tips.
3. The comma is not needed.
4. Change **leave** to **let**.
5. predicate adjective
6. Writers are encouraged to make use of the "Watston," the detective's assistant or friend, to help reveal clues to the reader.

7. Dr. Watson was Sherlock Holmes' friend and colleague.
8. The reader should know all clues.
9. Student should underline **clue** and **critical**.
10. Correct
11. Sentence 7

Lesson 32

1. B	6. G
2. H	7. D
3. A	8. G
4. J	9. B
5. C	

Lesson 33

A

1. 1, 2, 4
2. 1
3. globel - global
4. 2, 5
5. 7

B

1) *misplaced modifier and spelling error*
   Without the greenhouse effect, the earth might be 50° F colder.
2) *errors in subject-verb agreement, punctuation, use of adjective/adverb*
   The atmosphere has checks and balances; but carbon dioxide, a product of industry and cars; methane; nitrous oxide; and chlorofluorocarbon molecules in the atmosphere are increasing dramatically.
3) *no error*
   These gases could overwhelm any natural mechanisms that might moderate the effect.
4) *punctuation error*
   How does the greenhouse effect work?
5) *no error*
   Solar rays warm the Earth.
6) *no error*
   The Earth radiates infrared rays.
7) *spelling error*
   The warming rays are trapped, not released, into the atmosphere.

Lesson 34

A

1. One	4. Many
2. All	5. Several
3. most	

B

Everyone <u>says</u> the desert will return to its normal harsh climate. The Colorado River, a source of water for cities and farm irrigation from Denver to Los Angeles, is fueled by snow, but this has been the driest period in 98 years. Nobody <u>thinks</u> the water supply is adequate, but no one <u>is</u> addressing the problem. Someone <u>needs</u> to take action at the federal level to encourage states to solve the problem. Marinas at Arizona's Lake Powell, whose water levels are down 60 percent, are rebuilding boat ramps. Few <u>are</u> useless already—they lead to dirt, not water!

C

Some advocate for the dismantling of the dam; <u>they want</u> the river to return to its natural flow. Many know what will happen when water levels continue to fall; <u>they know</u> the sediments will be exposed, and weeds will soon fill the riverbed. Each state thinks <u>it has</u> the solution. One is filling <u>its</u> aquifers to save for a less rainy day. Another is removing <u>its</u>—an equivalent of a football field every day—from public places. Others are reducing <u>their</u> electrical power generation.

D

1. X
2. C
3. C
4. X

Lesson 35

A

1. Sea levels have risen nearly 560 feet since last ice age.
2. If all the Earth's ice melted, seas would rise almost 230 feet.
3. Global warming over the last hundred years has caused the sea level to rise almost 1/16 inch a year.
4. If seas rose only twenty inches in the next century, much of the Florida coastline would be submerged.
5. Between 1880 and 1980, the global mean sea level rose nearly four inches.
6. If the Antarctic ice sheet breaks and slips into the sea, giant waves would probably race toward the coastal areas.

B Possible answers:

1. The student could not stop writing in his essay about the flooding.
2. The student could not stop speaking in the hallway about global warming.
3. In the parking lot, the student could not stop asking questions about the intrusion of seawater.
4. The student could not stop searching on the Net for the effect of global warming on water supplies.
5. The student could not sleep in his bed without thinking about coastal erosion.

C Possible answers:

1. Checking the gauges every day, she carefully tracked the ice melt.
2. While doing their checks on the gauges, they liked to watch the penguins.
3. Without a plan for global warming, the scientists agreed that a conference seemed a good idea.
4. Fighting over a mate, the sea lions surprised the scientists.

Lesson 36

A

1. C
2. X
3. C
4. C
5. X

B

The article "Understanding *El Niño*" describes the phenomenon. The professor read it aloud to the student he was tutoring, "It is as an oceanic event that happens around Christmas along the western coast of South America. During this event, trade winds that occur in December slack off. This, in turn, causes a decrease in the water than rises from the depths of the ocean off the coast of Peru."

"Okay, then what?" she asked him.

He continued, "The waters become warm and nutrients die. It's the end of the peak fishing season. The impact on fisherman and entire communities can be severe, as it was during the 1982 season."

She wanted to know more, so she encouraged him to continue.

"That year was the most extreme *El Niño*. Not only did the fisheries in Peru and Chile fail, but the countries of Ecuador, Peru, Paraguay, Brazil, and Argentina also experienced floods. Plus, in the middle of the Pacific Ocean, cyclones hit the islands of Tahiti and Hawaii while droughts plagued part of Africa, India, Indonesia, and Australia."

C

1. !" 　　　 4. ."
2. ?" 　　　 5. ."
3. ."

Lesson 37

A

Answers will vary.

B

bases-baseball
basis-foundation
bearing-how you carry yourself
baring-to uncover
coarse-rough
course-subject
core-center
corps-military organization
council-organization
counsel-advise

C

cake-dessert 　　　 piece of cloth-canvas
chicken-fowl 　　　 scatter-disperse
in a book-foreward 　 smelly-foul
move-forward 　　　 survey-canvass
pay-disburse 　　　 leave-desert

D

1. X change aide to aid
2. C
3. X change bazaar to bizarre
4. X change cheep to cheap
5. C
6. X change rein to rain and miner to minor
7. X change medal to meddle

Lesson 38

A

1. P
2. D
3. C/E
4. E
5. A

B

Answers will vary.

Lesson 39

A Possible answer:

Dr. John Harrington described the continent of Antarctica as "an unspoiled landmass, perhaps the last on Earth." Despite this assertion, Antarctica faces severe challenges to its environment. Few disagree with this, but most cannot agree how to address its core challenges or how to prevent damage of this pristine environment. Dr. Harrington is looking forward to the debate. Bringing up the subject repeatedly at international conferences, he expresses his view that the future of the continent may be bright.

B

1. [answers may vary] The future of Antarctica depends upon the ability of the signatory nations of the Antarctic Treaty Body to adhere to the treaty's provisions.
2. [answers may vary] Activities on Antarctica are devoted to research, but treaty violations do occur.
3. 5
4. change **bands** to **bans** in sentence 4
5. change **sees** to **see** in sentence 7
6. "We cannot be complacent," the president said in his address to the international conference.

Lesson 40

A

1. A 　　　 6. H
2. G 　　　 7. C
3. D 　　　 8. G
4. J 　　　 9. B
5. C

Lesson 41

A

1. <u>Searching</u> through records made of stone is the way to date the disappearance of dinosaurs.
2. Scientists enjoy <u>searching</u> the strata beds for clues to a long-ago world.
3. Some have tried <u>tracing</u> the extinction to other causes, such as carbon dioxide buildup from volcanic eruptions.
4. What can we learn today by <u>studying</u> these environmental changes of a millennium ago?

B

1. subject
2. direct object
3. object of preposition
4. object of preposition

C

1. X
2. G
3. X
4. X
5. X
6. X
7. G
8. G

D
Answers will vary.

Lesson 42
A
1. X
2. They fell victim to millions of years of extreme conditions, climate changes, and unstable ecosystems.
3. Is it any coincidence that the arrival of man coincided with this great extinction, and is there growing evidence that man helped to hasten this great extinction of Ice Age mammals?
4. The Overkill Hypothesis is controversial, highly charged, and emotional.
5. X

B
1. An "endangered" species is one that will become extinct within the foreseeable future, and a "threatened" species is one that is likely to become endangered within the foreseeable future.
2. The World Conservation Union listed 5,205 animal species as either "critically endangered" or "vulnerable to extinction" in its 1996 report of threatened animals; this represented a huge increase in just six years.
3. Nine billion passenger pigeons filled the skies in 1850, but they were slaughtered by the millions for food and target practice.
4. The New York Zoological Society, the National Zoo, private reserves, and the Cincinnati Zoo rescued the American bison from a similar fate, or it, too, would not have survived to bear witness to our national heritage.

Lesson 43
A
1. Twenty colonizing species developed into the entire bird population of Hawaii, and many of the species they evolved into became flightless.
2. The flightless species fell victim to humans and habitation destruction, but scientists have found clear evidence of them in fossil records.
3. Since the arrival of Captain Cook in the islands in 1778, sixteen bird species have been lost, and 24 are listed as rare or endangered.

B
1. Hawaii's colonizing bird species, which arrived by flight from lands far away, diversified quite rapidly into new species, and none of them had to worry about predators.
2. When hungry humans arrived on the islands of Hawaii, they brought dogs with them; the flightless birds were soon in fear for their lives.
3. These birds, which had once been waterfowl, walked and waddled, but they did not fly.

C

1. The feathered caps of Hawaiian kings and queens, required the feathers of 80,000 birds; the preparation of these caps alone must have resulted in the extinction of species.
2. Throughout Hawaii on street corners, in schools, and near public buildings, you will find signs bearing a likeness of a Hawaiian king wearing a cap of pink feathers; is it a surprise that only nine native bird fauna remain from the hundreds that existed before humans arrived?
3. Scientists around the world are finding, excavating, and studying avian fossils; they are also discovering a pattern that links the arrival of man with the extinction of native species.

D
Answers will vary.

Lesson 44
A
1. He graduated from college in '99 with a degree in genetic engineering, but she studied for a graduate degree in paleontology from '97 to '03.
2. In the '70s, the United States passed an important law to help preserve species, and in '77, the international regulations under the Convention on International Trade in Endangered Species of Wild Fauna and Flora (CITES) took effect.
3. The American bald eagle was listed as endangered in 43 states in '78.

B
1. The scientist expressed himself clearly when he said, "We want to remember the words, 'We have nothing to fear, but fear itself,' as we undertake this important mission."
2. He ended his remarks with, "The results show which traits are inherited and which come from the environment—or as Dr. Johnson said, 'are derived from environmental constructs'—and are published in this report."
3. "I copied her inspiring words on the cover of my notebook, 'do the best your can,' and then started recording the genetic characteristics."

C
1. The scientists studied the fossil which measured approximately 8' x 10'.
2. The fossil of a dinosaur 5' high by 10' long was compressed into a space measuring 3' square.
3. If it were stretched straight, would our DNA strand reach 1,800'?
4. How many cubic yards are dirt are in a plot which measures 13' x 26'?

D
1. X
2. X
3. C
4. C
5. C
6. X

Answer Key

Lesson 45

A

1. X	6. C
2. X	7. C
3. X	8. X
4. X	9. C
5. C	10. C

B

1. gleaming	6. bitten
2. deferred	7. severely
3. getting	8. retained
4. conferring	9. taxing
5. folded	10. swagged

C

1. artfully	9. inferred
2. batting	10. inference
3. bloomer	11. marring
4. budded	12. mopped
5. canned	13. reference
6. clipped	14. transferee
7. controlling	15. tagged
8. fulfilling	

D

1. swatted or swatting
2. fitted or fitting
3. handicapped or handicapping
4. benefitted or benefiting
5. skied or skiing
6. omitted or omitting
7. equipped or equipping
8. flatted or flatting
9. excelled or excelling
10. clapped or clapping

Lesson 46

A

2 a.
1 b.
4 c.
5 d.
3 e.

B

d) Several environmental factors are affecting the survival of species.

C Possible answers:

1. There are several reasons why habitats are being destroyed.
2. How we develop as humans is determined by several factors.

D Answers will vary.

Lesson 47

A

1. '90s
2. Identifying all the genes in human DNA became the goal of the Human Genome Project.
3. • Completed in 2003 - dependent
   • the project was coordinated by the U. S. Department of Energy and the National Institutes of Health - independent
   • the Wellcome Trust from the United Kingdom was a major partner-independent
   • additional contributions came from Japan, France, Germany, china, and others - independent

B

1. verb
2. For example, studying genes will help us learn about the common biology that all life shares.
3. Comparing
4. For example, studying genes will help us learn about the common biology that all life shares, and comparing human genes with those of other organisms will help scientists identify genes that are associated with specific diseases and traits.
5. Will engineering a gene to reverse or arrest cancer be accomplished by scientists by the year 2010?
6. Possible answer: Scientists are working hard to solve some problems we humans face.

Lesson 48

1. B
2. H
3. C
4. H
5. C
6. G
7. B

Practice Test

1. A
2. H
3. B
4. F
5. D
6. H
7. A
8. B
9. G
10. C
11. H
12. C
13. F
14. D
15. H
16. C